Of Scientists and Salamanders

Adults of the California newt Taricha torosa torosa. *The smoother skin and prominent tail fin of the male (left) are secondary sexual differences that develop during the breeding season. Photograph by Thomas Rogers.*

Of Scientists and Salamanders

Victor Chandler Twitty

STANFORD UNIVERSITY

W. H. FREEMAN AND COMPANY
SAN FRANCISCO AND LONDON

TO | *JOHN McMAHON TWITTY*
      | *ROSS GRANVILLE HARRISON*

Foreword

A noted geneticist whose research required that he collect fruit flies in remote parts of the California backcountry had for years found difficulty in explaining his purpose to puzzled miners and ranchers, who clearly viewed his behavior as something less than mature. With the same genius that inspired his research he finally hit upon an answer that invariably satisfied them: "I get paid for it." I have occasionally borrowed this rejoinder in defending my devotion to another lowly animal, the salamander or newt.* But, obviously, there are other ways of making a living, and anyway, if one must collect things why choose fruit flies, or newts, of all things?

This is part of the larger question of what it is that launches a career in research and guides its course, and one of the objects of this book is to answer this in terms of my own modest but personally gratifying and entertaining experience. The role of chance in research and discovery is greater than is generally recognized, and this will be well exemplified as the narrative moves from New Haven to Berlin to Stanford, from microsurgery to natural history and back again, and from the study of cell populations in tissue culture to the study of animal populations in the streams and hills of northern California. It is not often that an investigator sits down and outlines a twenty-year project, and then

---

* As many readers will know, "salamander" is an inclusive name applicable to all tailed Amphibia (Caudata). The term "newt" is usually reserved for the rough-skinned species (such as Diemictylus of the eastern United States, Taricha of the west coast, and Triturus of Europe) of only one family of salamanders, the Salamandridae.

adheres to it for very long. For one thing, scientists, even illustrious ones, aren't usually that clever or far seeing. Also, it can be more exciting, and often more productive, to adapt one's course to new avenues opened up by unexpected observations in studies originally directed toward quite different goals. This is not as aimless and fickle as it sounds: in reviewing one's own work or that of others, it is interesting to look back and trace the steps that give continuity to an otherwise improbable sequence of investigations.

This is a book about the experimental biology of salamanders primarily as I have participated in it myself or have observed it at close range. I have chosen, without apology, to narrow the coverage in this way for the simple and possibly selfish reason that these are the animals and this is the work that I know best and happen to want to write about. I will confess, however, that it has not always been easy to remain within these bounds. My formal professional training was in embryology, and a substantial portion of the text will deal with experiments in that field. The abundance and variety of dramatic material afforded by developmental biology make it particularly difficult to adhere to the theme of personal identification that hopefully gives some measure of continuity and cohesiveness to the book. Perhaps I come closest to straying from the salamander trail as I have followed it myself when I present a short account of the so-called "organizer," a center in the amphibian embryo that directs the development of other parts. I justify this partly through my year's interlude of study in Germany with the school of Hans Spemann, discoverer of the organizer, as well as through a more direct personal involvement in the study of the organizer problem several years later. But the most compelling consideration is that any treatment of salamander biology that touches at all on the embryology of these animals would shame itself if it omitted reference to one of embryology's "finest hours." If the truth must be known, in an initial draft of the manuscript I became so carried away by the fascination of the organizer story that I gave it a full-scale treatment—only to be warned by a wise friend that this was totally in conflict with the announced design of the book. He pointed out—being careful not to imply whether this was for better or for worse—that "Twitty completely disappears." The unhappiness with which I performed the recommended extirpation, and numerous lesser ones that I have undertaken voluntarily, can be appreciated by any writer who has engaged in this cruel form of surgery.

Now that this pruning—and some grafting as well—has been completed, I hope the book will serve its intended purposes. (Perhaps I should explain here that the reason for the book, as distinguished from its purposes, is merely that I sat down one day, with almost no premeditation, and began to write it. Since then I have wished more than once that I had chosen that particular day to go fishing instead.) I have mentioned that one of these purposes is to illustrate how varied and unpredictable the circumstances that shape the course of a scientific career may be. Possibly my greatest piece of good luck came when I wandered into the orbit of Ross G. Harrison at Yale, and I hope my gratitude and admiration show through in the references I make to him and his work. I hope too that the reader senses how enjoyable it has been, and still is, to follow the salamander trail, and recognizes the fortitude with which I have accepted the vagaries of fate that have increasingly shifted my pursuit of newts from a basement laboratory at Stanford to the pleasant streams and mountains of Sonoma County. Only in an academic setting could I have had this freedom to "follow my nose" wherever it might lead me, and I am duly grateful for this unique and cherished privilege. Everything considered, I doubt that I could indeed have found better "ways of making a living."

In my blithe and optimistic allusions to "the reader," whom do I have in mind? I would like to think that the much sought-after and elusive "intelligent layman," with only a nodding acquaintance with biology, will find the book instructive and diverting, and I have tried to avoid technicalities that might intimidate him. I would also like to believe, however, that ample substance has been preserved to reward students and practitioners of biology. I hope that in weaving my way between these two audiences I have not evaded them both. The dilemma is almost an inescapable one, since I wish to advertise the virtues of my favorite animals as widely as possible, but cannot bring myself to sell them short by reducing the account of them to insubstantial levels.

Several friends, not all of them biologists, have been kind enough to read the manuscript or portions of it. It was Johannes Holtfreter, the eminent amphibian embryologist, who reminded me firmly that I had better deal more briefly with the Spemann epic lest the book and its author become irretrievably engulfed by it; I am grateful for this warning even though the resulting curtailment caused me much anguish. I am especially indebted to Viktor Hamburger, upon whom I inflicted both the initial and the final drafts of the manuscript, for his cogent and tactful counsel. Stanford colleagues Thomas Bailey, Norman Wessells, Peter Raven, and Donald Kennedy made constructive suggestions. I thank all of these, and others, for their help, and at the same time give them complete absolution from responsibility for defects I failed to remedy. Miss Sally Wilens, former research assistant to Professor Harrison, kindly supplied me with the portrait of him that appears on page 11, and also the striking photograph of one of his experimental animals reproduced as Figure 6, A. David Grant gave invaluable aid in preparing some of the histograms and photographs, and in construction of the index. Mr. Thomas Rogers generously permitted me to use his excellent color photograph of newts as a frontispiece for the book. Except as otherwise credited in the legends, the photographs are my own.

Contents

I

The Harrison Orbit

I suspect that the train of circumstances eventually leading me to newts had its remote and improbable beginnings in my father's conclusion that my devotion to basketball exceeded my dedication to scholarship, and that continued educational subsidy after high school promised meager returns on his investment. Bowing to this heresy (in Indiana basketball was—maybe still is —one of the ultimate values in life), I spent the first year following graduation from high school in the service of industry and finance. A meteoric rise during that period from factory flunky to filling-station attendant to bank teller (Christmas Savings cage!) transformed me into a painfully earnest young man and reawakened paternal hopes that there might be some scholarly possibilities here after all.

Two Lucky Choices

So now it was father instead of son who plugged the cause of education. By a shrewd challenge to my emerging idealism he led me to abandon banking and to enroll in college as a premedical student. We had moved from southern Indiana to Indianapolis not long before, and Butler College, which was immediately at hand, seemed an obvious choice. It was also a fortunate one. For one thing, I knew no one there and hence faced few social entanglements. Perhaps this was less important now that I had high resolve, but even so it was helpful. Had I started a year earlier, I would have gone to the state university with several high school classmates, and an active extracurricular future there had been augured by promise of membership in a fraternity quick to recognize and foster athletic prowess. This might have led eventually to a better or more significant destiny, but there can be no question that it would have been entirely different from the one that found its beginnings at Butler. Assuming on the basis of past performance that my academic potentialities were at best limited, and with no extracurricular involvements (some of these came later, fortunately) to interfere, I strove mightily in the modest hope that with luck I would at least get passing grades. Such obvious and sober purpose was bound to attract notice, as it did when midway in the first semester my botany teacher, Professor Ray Friesner, called me aside and hinted that if I maintained this pace, I might earn a pretty good mark in the course.

This astounding possibility, its realization, and similar results in all my other courses at the end of the semester, were all the ignition I needed to keep going at the pace I had established. At this time I decided that henceforth science, not medicine, was the road for me. Why my choice was eventually zoology— instead of chemistry, in which I actually majored, or botany, in which I had my first exposure to biology—I no longer clearly recall. But in any event I should like to record here my indebtedness to such Butler College professors as Ray Friesner, Guy Shadinger (chemistry) and Henry Bruner (zoology) for some of the most competent and dedicated teaching that I have encountered anywhere.

My choice of a college for undergraduate study was fortuitous but fortunate, and so was my choice of a university department for graduate training. Following a practice that still seems to be prevalent, I broadcast applications for fellowships or teaching assistantships to a half-dozen institutions. Some of these were selected partly because they were reasonably close to home, others because of the glamour of their very names. I believe that Chicago and Harvard may have had the strongest appeal, the former because I had just read a book [1] * by its celebrated (and controversial) Professor Charles Manning Child, and the latter because—well, I suppose largely just became it was Harvard. An offer of a tuition scholarship arrived from Chicago but left unresolved the matters of food and shelter. As for Harvard, my letter of application to Professor G. H. Parker of the Zoology Department was returned with-

---

* Bracketed numbers, such as this one, refer to Literature Cited, which begins on page 171.

out comment because I had failed to sign it! In his place I think I too might have felt that absent-mindedness was setting in a little *too* early in this would-be scholar. While I was still suffering from embarrassment and trying to decide whether to renew negotiations, a letter offering a teaching assistantship came from Professor Ross G. Harrison of Yale. Professor Bruner, on reading the letter, made a reverential reference to its writer, but the name was unknown to me and made no great impression. How was I to know that a man with no books—in particular, no textbooks—to his credit could be a scientist of unusual stature? But the combination of Yale University and six hundred dollars per year plus tuition was an attractive enough lure in itself, and although I didn't yet know it, the beginning of my association with salamanders was already in the offing.

My advent in New Haven in September 1925 was not auspicious. The first few days were spent in the eye ward at New Haven Hospital for observation of a sudden retinal inflammation that impaired vision in one eye. Then, at the first meeting of the freshman laboratory section assigned to my supervision I failed to recognize the youthful professor-in-charge and endeared myself by attempting to seat him with the students. But most of the graduate students were, like myself, from the hinterlands, the faculty was friendly and approachable, and I soon found the OZL (Osborn Zoological Laboratory) microcosm to be much less foreign and formidable than it had first appeared.

Its central figure and father image, Harrison himself, occupied a position of respect and affection that had already become legendary. To the generations of students who passed through the OZL during his reign, there could be only one "Chief," at Yale or elsewhere. His position in science was such that he was naturally held in considerable awe. (The story is told of the graduate student who was so afraid to address him that she could only watch in horror while bite by bite his spoon came closer to a fly imbedded in his banquet dessert.) But no one ever strove less to intimidate or impress, and if he seemed aloof it was merely that he was shy. I can remember the long and painful silences that sometimes developed during the bag luncheons over which he presided daily, and the Chief's obvious gratitude to any of us brash enough to end them by some desperate conversational gambit.

At Butler my zoological training had been mostly of the classical, descriptive variety, and accordingly I arrived at Yale with little preparation or bias that would predispose me in choosing among the areas of modern research specialization in the department. It is possible that there was already an incipient attraction to problems of embryonic development, aroused in part by the challenging book by Child referred to earlier, but I am sure that quite independently of this I would still have yielded to the pull of the Harrison gravitational field.

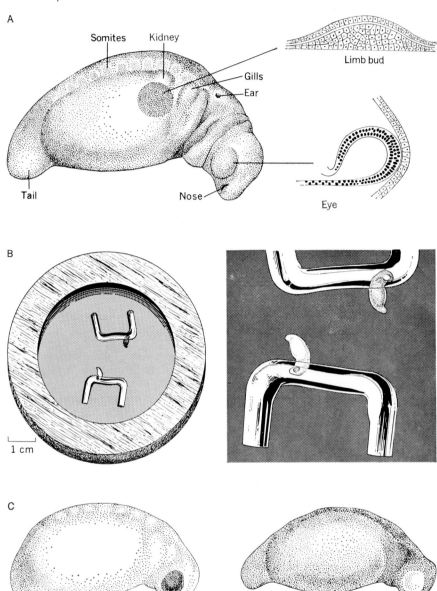

FIGURE 1. A: *An embryo in the "tail-bud stage" showing the locations of several organ rudiments that lend themselves readily to transplantation during this period of development. At the right are shown the two components of the limb bud (covering of epidermis and core of mesoderm) and the two parts of the eye rudiment (epidermis that later thickens and sinks inward to form the lens, and the sac-like extension from the forebrain*

The Microsurgeons

The reader will need no familiarity with the field of embryology to recognize the drama inherent in the transformation of egg into animal, and it was Harrison in this country, and Spemann in Germany, who were indisputably most responsible for initiating and giving direction to the modern analysis of vertebrate development. Both of them chose the amphibian embryo as an experimental object because it is of convenient size, develops almost nakedly (that is, within easily divested gelatinous capsules), lends itself well to surgical procedures, and is relatively resistant to infection. For reasons clearly traceable to their early training and experience, the two seized upon somewhat different approaches. Spemann undertook the study of the first stages of development and, accordingly, the emergence of the body plan in its primitive outline, while Harrison dealt primarily with the analysis of subsequent differentiations as the special organs and tissues gradually took more definitive form. For the experimental manipulations of these early rudiments Harrison adapted or developed surgical techniques that were to be fruitfully exploited for decades.

The parts of the embryo were soon parceled out, like mining claims in a new gold field, among Harrison's students and followers, and eye, ear, limb, nervous system, and other parts, each became a surgical specialty yielding a rich bonanza of information. It is not difficult to understand why surgery was so peculiarly and profitably applicable to problems of growth and form. As development proceeds, the embryo becomes an increasingly complex assemblage of structures, all emerging at the "right" times and places relative to one another to form an integrated pattern or configuration that we call frog, bird, or mouse. We learn little about the factors that guide this orderly process merely by observing and describing the manifold proliferations, shiftings, and foldings, that transform egg into organism. But if we disturb or rearrange the evolving system by excising selected parts or grafting them into new settings, we begin to expose some of the causal relationships and dependencies that were concealed. Since this is precisely what surgery, and surgery alone, permits the embryologist to do, what wonder that each spring the defenseless frog or salamander embryo

---

that becomes the retina). B: Wax dish in which embryonic surgery is performed. The embryos are placed in grooves adjusted to their size and shape, and after the grafts are transferred to the hosts they are held in position by arched glass rods for about ten minutes during the initial stages of healing. In this experiment eyes are being exchanged between embryos of two different species, and C shows two such embryos about thirty minutes after the bridges have been removed.

has been assaulted on all fronts by investigators resolved to leave none of its parts inviolate or in their accustomed contexts (Fig. 1).

A simple and classical example will illustrate the approach and the usefulness of the method. The retina of the eye originates as an outpocketing of the young brain tube. At the point where this sac pushes against the skin (epidermis) the latter thickens and pinches off as the rounded lens, fitting neatly within the rim of the developing retinal cup. Thus the lens and the retina, so intimately integrated henceforth as parts of a single organ, actually stem from quite different sources. No embryologist of imagination and curiosity could possibly resist inquiring into the basis of this collaboration between lens and retina. Is it merely fortunate coincidence, he might ask, that the lens arises precisely where it does, instead of at some other place on the head or body, or must there not be "instructions" issuing from the retinal sac or elsewhere that localize the site of lens formation and otherwise coordinate and synchronize the development of the eye components? Only by placing the embryo on the operating table can answers to such questions be wrung directly and successfully from it. If we suspect that the retinal sac somehow triggers lens development it is simple enough to remove it surgically and wait to see whether a lens forms. The same question can be asked of the embryo in another way, by excising the area of the epidermis that would normally form the lens and replacing it by epidermis from another region of the body. The upshot of these and numerous other surgical maneuvers is the discovery that the site of lens formation is indeed localized by stimuli from neighboring tissues, notably the retinal sac itself [2]. The act by which one tissue or organ specifies the fate of another is commonly called embryonic "induction," and the retinal sac is only one of a multitude of "inductors" that channel the parts of the embryo along their diverse pathways. The eye itself, if we include its other components and associated structures such as the cornea, the ocular muscles, the coats that invest the eyeball, and the brain centers to which it is linked by the optic nerve, is particularly replete with examples of unilateral or reciprocal dependencies that shape organic form [3].

The surgical methods and paraphernalia employed in these studies are relatively simple, and a short internship is usually enough to bring proficiency. The operating table is the stage of a binocular dissecting microscope. Viewed through lenses that magnify the object ten to twenty times, an embryo measuring only two or three millimeters in diameter or length looms large enough to permit recognition and manipulation of tiny parts of its anatomy. For the most part "organs" do not yet exist as such, but familiarity with embryonic topography tells one the location of the patches or clumps of cells that are later to form lens, nose, brain, ear, kidney, and limb. The cutting instruments used depend to some extent on the age of the embryo and the toughness or texture of its tissues. In very early stages their almost butter-like consistency yields readily to sharp but fragile glass needles, but stronger instruments, preferably the expertly sharpened tips of the small iris shears used for surgery on the human eye, are more effective tools for use on older embryos. After a shallow incision is made around the periphery of an organ rudiment it is teased free with sharp steel needles and transferred to a wound site previously prepared on the same or another embryo. Here it is held in position during healing by arched strips of glass. No sutures are needed, healing is rapid, and within less than an hour it is often difficult to discern the original line of incision. There is no need for anaesthesia, or concern about bleeding, since the embryo has not yet acquired nerves or blood. Sterile precautions, such as washing the embryos free of bacteria before use by pipetting them through several changes of boiled water, are often necessary when operating on very young embryos, but become less important as older subjects are used. And if some experimental subjects die, from whatever causes, the situation is not disastrous; one merely disposes of the embryos and brings in a new batch from the nearest pond or stream.

Tissue Culture—Invented for a Purpose

Harrison's most widely heralded series of personal researches was probably the one culminating in the invention of the tissue-culture method and its use to settle a classical problem, determining the manner in which nerve fibers arise and attain their relatively vast lengths. A microscopic thread issuing from the spinal cord and extending the length of a frog's leg, to say nothing of that of a man or giraffe, is after all an entity of such unique proportions that one can understand the difficulty encountered by nineteenth- and early twentieth-century morphologists in harmonizing its structure with the cell theory. Could this long strand possibly be an extension of a single cell, as one school maintained, or was it not more reasonable to assume that it is the joint product of many cells, which perhaps fuse end-to-end and sacrifice their individual identities to provide an unbroken transmission line between remote parts of the body?

Harrison believed strongly that the evidence favored the first of these alternatives, namely that cells in the brain and spinal cord and in their closely associated ganglia sprout filamentous spikes that grow to whatever length is necessary to span the distances between the central nervous system and peripheral parts of the body. But the evidence for this was largely circumstantial, and it was obvious that the stubborn opposition forces would be swayed by nothing short of direct proof or demonstration. This Harrison set out to supply, by ingenious but essentially simple surgical experiments with the frog embryo. If nerve fibers grow from cells in the central nervous system, then embryos deprived of this system should remain nerveless. If, on the other hand, fibers are built up from cell types other than those found in the nervous system, then absence of the central nerve tube ought not preclude the appearance of fibers in limbs or other outlying structures. The excision of the brain and cord seems even now like rather radical surgery, but Harrison did it successfully, and kept the subjects alive and growing by uniting them in Siamese-twin fashion with normal embryos.

In keeping with the "outgrowth theory" these parasitic twins remained nerveless. If he used them as hosts for pieces of embryonic spinal cord, fibers appeared around the grafts but nowhere else. And obstructions grafted into the pathway between spinal cord and limb rudiments of normal embryos resulted in nerveless appendages [4].

As clear as it now seemed from these and related experiments that nerve cells, and nerve cells alone, can form nerves, no one had yet really *seen* them in the act of spinning out these long fibers. In fact, one might even maintain that nerve cells are necessary to nerve formation not because they actually yield the fibers themselves but because they somehow stimulate other cell types to do so.

Any stalemate that might have threatened to develop at this point was soon resolved by Harrison's invention of the method of tissue culture. The nerve cells might effectively cloak their behavior while hiding within the organism (*in vivo*), but Harrison denied them this obscurity by plucking them from the embryo and growing them nakedly outside the body (*in vitro*). He could at last watch directly as bits of spinal cord isolated in drops of clotted blood or lymph sprouted extensions that spun themselves into longer and longer threads (Fig. 2) whose identity as nerve fibers could not be questioned [5].

One can only guess what Harrison's sensations were when he encountered the first culture exhibiting this phenomenon. They must have been exalted, and one almost hopes that for once he shed his modesty and restraint and in the privacy of his laboratory uttered at least an audible "Eureka!" It was indeed an epochal accomplishment. Not only did it establish once and for all the individual nerve cell as the unit of nervous-system structure and function, but it also made available a method, tissue culture, that has since become an invaluable research tool in many fields of experimental biology and medicine. It is an interesting footnote, incidentally, that Harrison's first successful nerve cultures were followed by a few that failed for one technical cause or another.

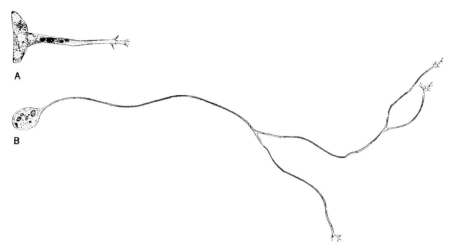

FIGURE 2. A: *Nerve fiber beginning to grow out from a cell forming part of a small cell mass isolated in a drop of clotted lymph.* B: *A few days later, after the nerve fiber has become branched and greatly elongated.* (*After Figs. 7 and 22, R. G. Harrison, J. Exp. Zool.,* **9.**)

I heard him say later that if this order had been reversed he might well have abandoned the whole effort. But I doubt it!

The Harrison Approach

Harrison did not tarry long in tissue culture. He had invented it for a specific purpose, and once this had been served he left its exploitation to others and proceeded about his main business, the study of embryonic development and differentiation. It would have been out of keeping with Harrison's character and approach to science if he had allowed himself to be enticed away from this study into any of the many avenues that were undoubtedly opened to his fertile imagination through discovery of a new and highly versatile technique.

Much has been said and written about what it is that motivates scientific investigation. Consuming curiosity, thirst for Truth, desire to aid mankind, or just the plain fun of research and discovery—all of these and others are commonly mentioned as the driving forces, and I do not doubt that in proportions varying with the background and temperament of the individual scientist all may play their roles. But if I had to identify a single factor that made Harrison's work great, I would do it in terms of aesthetic considerations. He was constitutionally incapable of leaving a project until all its pieces had been fitted into a unitary whole whose composition met his artistic requirements. Stated more prosaically, this could mean merely that he had a strong sense of order or organization, which was indeed true. (Although his office desk was often badly cluttered, to the despair of his secretary, this was never true of his research bench, of his research records, or of his mind.) More than most scientists, I believe, he both required and created an element of beauty in the form and perfection of his experimental analyses. It might even be said that this was sometimes carried to excess, as if he insisted on adding minor brush strokes to a masterpiece whose major features and import were already abundantly clear. But if there was possibly some unnecessary detail within his masterpieces, their boundaries were left sharp and unencumbered.

Many biologists (and most assuredly *all* of his students) consider it an injustice that Harrison was never awarded the Nobel Prize for his invention of tissue culture. Jane Oppenheimer [6], a former student at Osborn Laboratory, has recently called attention to records showing that in 1917, when the prizes lapsed because of World War I, a majority of the Nobel Prize Committee had favored giving the award to Harrison. In 1933 his name again came before the Committee, which however rendered an unfavorable decision "in view of the rather limited value of the method." Considering subsequent developments, including the award of the Prize in 1954 for studies on the growth of virus infections in tissue culture, one would be prompted to wonder how wrong committees can be—if one did not already know from having served on so many.

But Harrison received honors aplenty, and it was not within his modest and generous nature to harbor any bitterness over such matters. It was perhaps because of his self-effacement that *Fortune,* in an article about Yale University, could characterize him as "America's most famous unknown scientist."

"ASK MORGAN, *He* KNOWS"

As an example of his humility, I am reminded of an incident during his visit to Stanford in 1939 to take part in an international symposium celebrating the one-hundredth anniversary of the enunciation of the cell theory. Scheduled to speak late in the course of the symposium, he arrived with only sketchy notes and a suitcase full of scientific literature dealing with his topic. He was a guest in our home, and we made every effort to afford him seclusion until he could complete preparation of his lecture. A room was set aside as his study, and strict instructions were issued to our four young children to respect his privacy. But the fascination of the program and the social activities accompanying the symposium proved irresistible to him, and with each day his concern—

FIGURE 3. *Ross Granville Harrison in 1911, shortly after his invention of tissue culture.*

and mine—for the lecture continued to mount. He was head of the National Research Council at the time, and the flood of neglected correspondence that arrived in each mail from Washington helped aggravate his feeling of frustration and inadequacy. After breakfast on the day of his lecture he was in a mood of deep discouragement. "Twitty, you know what's wrong with me, don't you?" Not knowing how else to respond, I mumbled something to the effect that I wished I were lucky enough to suffer some of the same ailments. "No," he said, in all earnestness, "I'm *lazy*." To understand my discomfiture, try to bear in mind that the man denouncing himself to me in these terms was Ross Granville Harrison, recipient of honorary degrees from several American and European universities, and a Foreign Member of the Scientific Academies of England, Norway, Sweden, and The Netherlands, and of the Academia dei Lincei and the Academie des Sciences of the Institut de France. All that I could do in my embarrassment was to pretend amusement, but Dr.

Harrison was not joking. In a tone as nearly vehement as he was capable of, he insisted, "No, no, you ask Morgan [T. H. Morgan, close friend and illustrious geneticist], *he'll* tell you. *He* knows." As Michael Abercrombie remarked in an admirable biographical memoir prepared for the Royal Society [14], "No wonder that Ross Harrison captured the devotion of so many."

Symmetry and Salamander Legs

When I arrived at Osborn Laboratory, fifteen years after publication in 1910 of Harrison's classical "The Outgrowth of the Nerve Fiber as a Mode of Proto-plasmic Movement," [5] tissue culture was no longer a prominent activity there, and he and his students had already been engaged for a decade or more in their surgical explorations of organ development. For this purpose the embryos of the spotted salamander, *Amblystoma punctatum,** had proved to be better suited than frog embryos, and articles whose titles incorporated the name of this now famous experimental animal appeared in almost all issues of the *Journal of Experimental Zoology,* which Harrison had helped found and still directed as managing editor. "Amblectomists"—the practitioners of *Amblystoma* surgery—who had passed through OZL on their way to prominence included Harold Burr, Robert Burns, Wilfred Copenhaver, Samuel Detwiler, Davenport Hooker, John Nicholas, Leon Stone, and Frank Swett.

Principally as a training exercise in amblectomy, Professor Harrison assigned me a small project that exemplified in perhaps the simplest possible terms an aspect of development, the polarity and symmetry of embryonic organs, that had become one of his major interests. We accept it as normal that the limb, for instance, grows out in the right relationship to the body, instead of upside down or hindside before. This is not mere happenstance, and Harrison explored the matter with typical thoroughness and imagination.

The limb develops from a disc-shaped area of tissue separable into two layers, a superficial sheet of "ectoderm" that becomes the epidermis of the appendage, and an underlying one of "mesoderm" from which all the other main structures except nerves are derived. The disc (Fig. 1) is not visibly delimited at first from the surrounding expanses of ectoderm and mesoderm, but it can be located by certain landmarks on the embryo. The ectodermal part plays a

* The current spelling of this genus name, by taxonomists and by most experimental biologists, is *Ambystoma* instead of *Amblystoma*. My adherence to the latter spelling is in deference to Professor Harrison's unyielding insistence that in the original christening of the genus the omission of the *l* was a typographical error. In the spirit of the present book it somehow seems inappropriate to depart from Harrison's own spelling of the name he made so famous.

relatively passive role, in that epidermis from other regions can be substituted for it without interfering with normal limb development. The future of the mesodermal component is, however, already firmly fixed, since it persists in forming a limb no matter where it may be grafted on the body. Although tadpoles with legs growing on their heads or in other strange sites may indeed look ludicrous, and may even arouse speculation whether the motives of the surgeon were serious or whimsical, these bizarre creatures are designed to instruct, not to divert, and the simple demonstration that the limb disc can indeed realize its destiny in foreign locations has considerable significance. It means the quality of "limbness" is already localized in the mesodermal disc long before its cells show any evidence of differentiation, and, moreover, that this quality or potentiality can achieve full expression without dependence

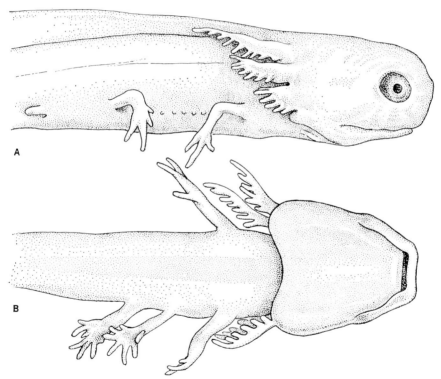

FIGURE 4. A: *A supernumerary limb that has grown out "hindside before" as a result of being grafted in reversed orientation at an early embryonic stage. (After Fig. 18, R. G. Harrison, J. Exp. Zool.,* **32:**18.) *B: Two supernumerary limbs developing from a single limb bud that was split in half before grafting. (After Fig. 11, F. H. Swett, J. Exp. Zool.,* **52:** 147.)

on influences peculiar to the limb region [7]. The limb disc is, then, a "*self-differentiating*" system.

Harrison's experiments enabled him to add another very important adjective to the description of the disc. When he cut out half of the disc, say the anterior half or the dorsal half, and grafted it elsewhere, it formed not a half limb but a normal whole one (Fig. 4, B). Likewise, the half disc that was left undisturbed also formed an entire appendage. In other words, the limb disc is a self-differentiating, *equipotential* system, with all parts of it equivalent in their capacity to form a whole limb or any portion thereof. In the beginning, then, "the limb's the thing," not the individual destinies of the parts of the disc; these remain to be sorted out and assigned through interactions and agreements that are worked out within the disc as it continues on its course toward actual limb formation.

Any of the axes of the limb disc can be reversed singly or in any combination by appropriate maneuvers [8]. If it is simply rotated through a half turn, it is now both upside down and hindside before in relation to the embryo. If, however, the disc is switched from one side of the embryo to the other, without rotating it at all, it will now be upside down but not hindside before. (Try this with a coin, representing the limb disc, and any two-sided object such as a book, representing the embryo). If it is shifted from one side to the other, and at the same time rotated 180 degrees, it is now hindside before but not upside down. The possibilities don't end here. In the manipulations just described, the outer and inner faces of the disc were not reversed in relation to the embryo; if the mesodermal layer of the disc is exposed and its outer face turned inward, an even more dramatic possibility presents itself. It is one thing for a limb to grow out hindside before or upside down, but could it conceivably also grow, not *out from* the embryo, but *inwards* toward the depths of the embryo?

The limb is thus assembled, as it were, along three lines or axes, one running from upper surface to lower (dorso-ventral axis), a second from frontside to hind (antero-posterior axis), and a third along its length, from the body outwards (medio-lateral axis). And no limb, no matter how perfectly and completely constructed, is a normal limb unless all these axes are properly related to those of the animal itself [9]. To the embryologist this poses the question of when and how this harmony and correspondence of pattern is imposed on the developing limb disc.

Harrison and Swett showed that the three axes of its development are fixed, not simultaneously, but during distinctly different periods in the early life of the embryo. The antero-posterior axis is "determined" first; in fact, no matter how early in development this axis of the disc is surgically reversed the result-ing limb grows out hindside before (Fig. 4, A). Possibly the fore-and-aft aspect of limb structure is fixed at the same time the limb-destiny itself of the disc is established. Reversal of the dorso-ventral axis in the earliest stages does not disturb the normal orientation of the ensuing leg; it still grows out right-side-up. Only when the same experiment is performed at a significantly later stage in development does the reversal manifest itself in an upside down appendage. In the interval between the two experiments, word has gone out from embryo to disc, that henceforth directs its development along increasingly inflexible lines. Ingenious experiments by Nicholas showed that the polarizing influence emanates from the tissues immediately surrounding the limb disc, not from the embryo as a whole. But the nature of the influence, and of the invisible physical or chemical changes it produces in the cells of the disc, is still obscure. Harrison proposed that the configuration of the limb is an expression of under-lying molecular, essentially crystalline, configurations in the cytoplasm of the disc cells. Efforts to test this by X-ray-diffraction analysis were unsuccessful, but this is not surprising in view of the technical difficulties inherent in the material.

Polarization of the medio-lateral axis follows closely upon fixation of the dorso-ventral axis. If the reader is still trying to visualize the consequences of reversing the faces of the limb disc after this polarization has occurred, he will be relieved to know that the limb does *not* grow inward. In turning to avoid this fate, however, the limb grows out in an abnormal orientation, and thus reveals that the medio-lateral axis had indeed become fixed before the disc was reversed.

Baptismal Research Project

The aspect of polarity assigned to me for study was the direction of stroke of the cilia that adorn the epidermis of the young embryo. These microscopic, swiftly beating hairlike structures are standard equipment in all vertebrate animals in certain internal passageways such as the genital ducts and trachea, but they are present externally only on the amphibian embryo and larva. When they first grow out and begin to beat, their presence is manifested by the rotation of the embryo within its capsule, and their agitation of the capsular fluid undoubtedly facilitates the exchange of respiratory gases between embryo and water. The effective strokes of the cilia are in general directed posteriorly and thus create a backward flow of water over the surface of the skin (Fig. 5).

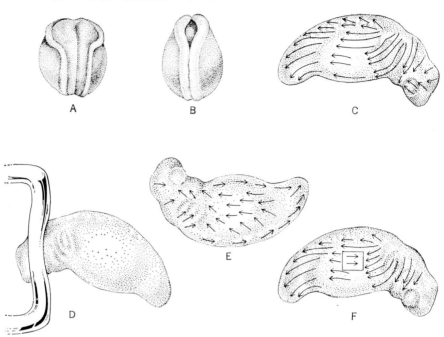

FIGURE 5. A: *The large area of dorsal ectoderm bordered by the horseshoe-shaped ridge becomes the central nervous system of the embryo. B: The two arms (neural folds) move together and eventually fuse to form the tubular brain and spinal cord. C: The arrows show the direction of water currents created by the rapidly beating cilia on the epidermis of the embryo. These cilia propel the embryo headfirst along the bottom of the operating dish or other substratum, but if the forward motion is prevented by a slightly arched glass "bridge" placed over the head (D), the direction of ciliary beat reverses (E) and the embryo escapes by backing out from under the bridge. F: If a square of epidermis is reversed early in development (before the stage in part B, above), the cilia later developing on the graft beat in the normal direction; but if a piece of epidermis is rotated at a later stage of development its cilia beat in a reversed direction. (After Twitty [11].)*

When the embryo is removed from its envelope and placed in the wax-bottomed dishes used for surgery, the cilia often propel the patient head-first across the bottom of the dish while the surgeon pursues it with his shears.

My first task was to rotate squares or discs of epidermis to see whether, as in the polarization of limb development, there is a critical stage at which the direction of ciliary beat becomes fixed. What could be simpler than to make a rectangular incision, lift up the piece of ectoderm thus outlined, reverse it end-for-end, and heal it in again? But Dr. Harrison had neglected to tell me that the piece might stick like glue to the underlying mesoderm, that once freed it would often fold promptly into a tight scroll, that in trying to unroll it I might tear it into shreds or lose track of which end was which, and that, having finally gotten the graft in position, it was *quite* likely that I would crush both it and its host by inexpert application of the glass bridges used as weights during healing. (I was not the first to learn that the Chief, kindly as he was, did not exactly smother his students with care and supervision.) Before long, however, these difficulties inexplicably began to diminish, and my first piece of research was under way [11].

The direction of ciliary beat on the grafts was ascertained by pipetting suspensions of powdered carbon or carmine on them and observing the displacement of the particles. It turned out that the direction of beat was concordant with that on the surrounding host skin if the piece had been rotated early enough, but discordant (in the reversed direction) if the rotation was performed later (Fig. 5, F). The "moment of decision" at which the beat became polarized proved to be in the stage of development when the primitive nerve tube first forms (Fig. 5, B), only a short time before the actual emergence of the cilia on the skin. As with the limb, we do not know what the influence is that strikes the epidermis at this critical stage, but it is apparently a sweeping one; at this same time the antero-posterior axis of the ectodermal inner ear is fixed, as is the direction of migration of the ectodermal cells that move posteriorly from the head to form the sensory "lateral line" system of the trunk (Stone).

The role of chance in research and discovery will be illustrated several times in this book. I encountered an example of it in this first foray into embryonic surgery. The very feature of an embryo that attracts our interest, namely that it changes and develops, can also be a source of embarrassment and practical difficulty to the embryologist. If he is not alert, he may find that embryos set aside yesterday afternoon, for surgery today, have passed overnight beyond the stage needed for his purposes. Retardation of development by lowered temperature is the only means for averting this possibility. At the time embryos are brought in from the field, it is common and provident practice to divide them into lots for storage at different temperatures. Toward the end of the amphibian breeding season, the only young embryos available in the laboratory may be those that have been refrigerated, and it happened that one of my series of ectodermal transplantations was made with such icebox material. To my surprise I found that in these embryos ciliary polarity had become fixed, not in the nerve tube stage as before, but appreciably earlier, while the thickened plate of ectoderm destined to form the nerve tube was still an open and shallow trough on the dorsal surface of the embryo (Fig. 5, A). The effect of the cold, then, had been to slow down the visible or gross anatomical changes of development more than it had slowed down the progress of the invisible, presumably chemical, changes that polarize the ciliary beat. Thus, I discovered—partly through the chance determination that a particular experiment was performed at a time when embryos of the proper age were not available in their natural environment—that temperature can be used to change the gearing between the morphological and chemical events of development. This device was employed, many years later, by one of my students (Antone Jacobson [12]) and others in resolving a highly confusing and paradoxical aspect of the classical problem of lens induction.

I shall pass over other surgical experiments that I performed [13] on the problem of ciliary polarity, except for one other part of this baptismal research project that I cannot bring myself to leave unmentioned. Dr. Harrison had noted, as others possibly had, that embryos pinioned by glass bridges placed over their heads (Fig. 5, D) to hold grafts in place often escaped by backing out from under them. Since this is contrary to the normal direction of move-ment, he suggested that I look into the possible ciliary basis of the phenomenon. And when I duplicated the conditions producing the response, the first pipette-full of carmine particles was enough to reveal that the cilia were indeed the culprits. They had reversed their direction of beat and thus had propelled the embryo backwards and away from the impediment that had blocked normal forward motion.

Only the cilia on the parts of the ectoderm in contact with the dish or bridge participated in the reversal (Fig. 5, E), and it was apparently the resistance offered to the cilia by these surfaces that triggered the change in direction of beat. Support for this explanation came from the response of embryos placed in a dense, unyielding medium (quince-seed jelly). Here, 180-degree reversal of the cilia would accomplish nothing, since an embryo could not move backward in this medium any more readily than it could move forward. Instead, the embryo in the jelly rotated on its long axis, like a pig on a spit, and examination showed that the ciliary currents girdled the embryo in a con-tinuous flow that moved dorsally on one side and ventrally on the other. Modi-fiability of ciliary behavior thus provides a fortunate escape from frustration and futility.

When an embryo is removed from cramped or other experimental situations that cause ciliary reversal, the normal direction of beat is soon restored. If, during the period in which the direction is changing, the area of ectoderm showing reversal is free of contact with the surface that caused the beat to reverse, the resumption of normal beat is preceded by a state of confusion, with no concert in the direction of beat of the cilia on different cells. But if the contact persists, as when an embryo that has backed out from under a bridge is left in undisturbed contact with the dish except for periodic examination of its underside, the cilia on this surface are found to be beating in unison as the direction of beat swings gradually through 180 degrees. The original reversal is also accomplished in this orderly manner. This concerted behavior should not be attributed to integration by nervous or other intercommunication between the participating cells. There are, in fact, no nerves in the embryo at this early stage, and experiments showed that coordination persists within an area of contact even when parts of the area are isolated from one another by gaping incisions. The simplest explanation of the coordination is that the cilia of different cells beat in concert during reversal and recovery merely because they encounter the least environmental resistance by doing so.

Altogether, the ciliary project was a rewarding and entertaining initiation into experimental biology. I suspect that embryologists will find it profitable to return to these organelles when methods become available for effectively attacking phenomena of cellular polarity at the molecular level.

"A Simple and Original Idea"

Another of Harrison's major research activities at the time was the use of organ transplantation for the study of proportionate growth. We have already seen examples of how surgically revealed interactions between parts of the organism affect their *quality* (whether, for example, an area of epidermis does or does not form a lens, whether or not a limb is harmoniously oriented, and so on), but surgery is also uniquely suited for analysis of the more strictly quantitative aspects of animal form. Steel shears and needles do not, of course, lend themselves to studies of the chemical nature of the growth process, but "growth" encompasses much more than the mere manufacture of new building materials. If sheer synthesis were all that is involved, we would grow up into spherical aggregates of bone, muscle, eye, brain, and kidney that even a mother might find difficult to love. It is the *differential* growth of parts, according to a pattern characteristic for each species, that saves us from this fate, and the factors that regulate distribution of growth between head and trunk, nose and face, and foot and shank, are accordingly the subject of legitimate concern and interest.

Needless to say, surgery cannot work miracles in attacking a problem of this scope, but Harrison and his students made some real inroads into it, as testified by Abercrombie [14] in the biographical memoir of Harrison already cited. "The whole body of work, though it has revealed more problems than solutions, is probably the most extensive experimental attack on the growth of

A

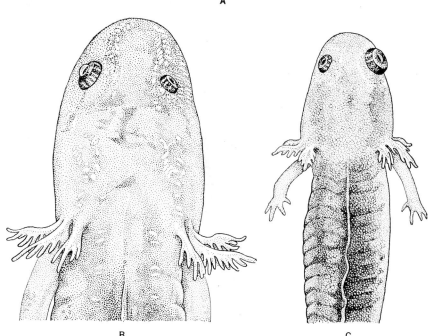

B   C

FIGURE 6. A: *Larva of* Amblystoma punctatum *bearing a right limb grafted in the embryonic stage from the much more rapidly growing* Amblystoma tigrinum. (*After Fig. 13, R. G. Harrison, Heteroplastic Grafting in Embryology. The Harvey Lectures. 1933–34, Ser. 29, p. 146.*) *Right eyes exchanged between embryos or young larvae of the rapidly growing* Amblystoma tigrinum (B) *and the slowly growing* Amblystoma punctatum (C) *adhere to their hereditary growth rates and hence become much smaller or much larger than the normal eyes of their hosts.* (*After Figs. 8 and 11, R. G. Harrison, Correlation in the de-*

animal organs yet made, based on a characteristically simple and original idea of Harrison's." This simple and original idea was to transplant organs, or parts of organs, between embryos of slowly and rapidly growing species, especially between the spotted salamander (*Amblystoma punctatum*) and the tiger salamander (*Amblystoma tigrinum*).

Although the embryos of these two species are of approximately the same size initially, the rates of subsequent differentiation and growth are much faster in *tigrinum*. With this pair of salamanders at his disposal Harrison could begin to ask some penetrating questions about size relations within the body. For example, does the *tigrinum* eye or limb grow faster and become larger than the corresponding *punctatum* organ merely because it has a greater inherent growth potential, or, instead, because it has the advantage of being situated on an animal that is eating more and growing faster itself? Is it, in other words, primarily a matter of "nature," or of "nurture"? The way to put the question to a test, obviously, is to place the *tigrinum* organ on a *punctatum* host and see whether nature or nurture wins out. This question cannot be readily asked of "more important" pairs of animals, such as quail and goose, or mouse and rabbit, because in these higher animals the laws of immunology are in full operation and the alien grafts would be recognized and destroyed before clear answers could be obtained. But in *Amblystoma* and many other salamanders, immunological barriers are lacking or feeble and interfere little or not at all with the continuing health and welfare of the transplanted organs.

The outcome of Harrison's initial experiments was aptly characterized by an adjective in the title of his first paper on the subject, "Some *unexpected* results of the heteroplastic transplantation of limbs" [15]. Not only did the *tigrinum* appendage grow as well on the small *punctatum* host as when left in its normal setting, it seemed to do considerably better! In other words it became not only immensely larger than the opposite, normal limb of the small host, but substantially larger than the control limb left growing on the large *tigrinum* donor (Fig. 6, A). And limbs grafted reciprocally, from *punctatum* to *tigrinum*, were not only much smaller than those of their hosts, they did not even keep pace with those on the small *punctatum* donors. This same situation proved to apply also to eyes grafted between embryos of the same two species.

To explain the seeming paradox Harrison tentatively postulated that organ growth is the product of two primary factors. One of these, the "growth potential," or inherited growth impetus, is intrinsic to the cells of the organ. The sec-

velopment of the eye, studied by means of heteroplastic transplantation, Arch. EntwMech. Org., **120**:13. *1929; and after Twitty and Elliott* [18].)

ond, the growth "regulatory factor," is extrinsic to the organ and might be a hormonal agent circulating in the blood stream. The growth potential was obviously stronger in the organs of the larger *tigrinum,* but the incentive to its expression, the regulatory factor, was evidently more powerful in the smaller *punctatum;* hence the overgrowth of *tigrinum* organs exposed to the milieu provided by *punctatum,* and the retarded growth of *punctatum* organs subjected to the less favorable growth environment afforded by *tigrinum.*

Harrison wanted a further check on his results, and a fellow graduate student and I enrolled at Yale at just the right time to fall heir to the problem as the basis for our doctoral research projects. The limb was assigned to Joseph Schwind and the eye to me, and the partnership later sometimes referred to as Schwitty and Twind thus came into being.

When spring arrived we exchanged the organs between embryos of *punctatum* and *tigrinum* in the so-called "tail-bud" stage, at which time the forelimb is still merely the two-layered disc of cells mentioned earlier, and the eye a simple vesicle (future retina) capped by a disc of epidermis that will form the lens. Because it is smaller, and simpler in shape, the eye can be measured more easily and accurately than the limb by a fine scale inserted in the eyepiece of a microscope. From the time that the differentiating grafts were first clearly outlined against the more transparent host tissue their size was compared at weekly intervals with that of the donor control eyes.

As time progressed, I became puzzled by the close correspondence that continued to exist between the dimensions of the organs in their normal and foreign settings. The grafted *tigrinum* eyes, for example, although much larger than the opposite organs of their *punctatum* hosts, remained strikingly similar in size to the normal eyes of the *tigrinum* larvae that had donated them. I thought I must have done something wrong, but when I returned from the marine laboratory where both the larvae and I had spent the summer, I learned that Schwind was in the same quandary over the behavior of his limb grafts.

On comparing notes with Dr. Harrison we found that the *tigrinum* larvae had grown faster, relative to those of *punctatum,* in our experiments than in his, and the explanation of his earlier results eventually proved to be as simple as this: The young man who helped Harrison feed his animals, not fully recognizing the enormous difference in the appetites of the two species, had supplied a diet that more nearly satiated the *punctatum* than it did the *tigrinum* larvae. This meant that *tigrinum* eyes and limbs grafted to *punctatum* were being compared with organs growing on *tigrinum* donors which, although eating more, were still relatively underfed and thus afforded faulty controls for the comparisons. Schwind and I, through no conscious effort, happened to feed the larvae in amounts that were apparently more in keeping with the differing appetites of the two species, and organs grafted between them seemed to find their new setting no more nor no less favorable than their accustomed one.

But at first we could not be sure that there might not still be an element that made our results unreliable. Wasn't it possible, for example, that with this readjustment of diet the *punctatum*, not the *tigrinum*, were now being discriminated against? How *does* one go about insuring that two species with different eating habits will grow at rates that accurately reflect the difference in their hereditary growth endowments? It was decided that the only simple solution was to keep both species fully satiated at all times, by keeping food constantly available or proffering it so frequently that there could be no charge of discrimination or possibility of unrequited hunger.

When this practice was instituted the following spring, with new series of hosts, the results confirmed our first findings: The grafted eyes (Fig 6, B, C) and limbs did indeed grow at rates virtually identical to those of the donor control organs [17]. "Maximal feeding" became standard procedure in all subsequent experiments requiring comparisons of organ growth in normal and foreign settings.

Was the conclusion, then, that Harrison's regulatory factor is nonexistent and that organ growth is an expression solely of inherent genetic constitution? Obviously not, since this would in effect be saying that the growth of the part is unrelated to the growth of the whole, and one can hardly conceive that an animal takes shape quite as haphazardly as this. If eyes and limbs grafted between *punctatum* and *tigrinum* continue to grow at their accustomed rates, it is presumably not because their growth is independent of environmental regulation, but because the regulating factors are so similar in the two species that they do not trigger observable differences in the transplanted organs.

This situation is exceptional. One would hardly expect that a given organ would find precisely the same conditions for growth on all species to which it might be grafted, or that the environmental factors regulating growth would necessarily be the same for different organs. And, in fact, Detwiler reported that when even a slightly different geographical strain of *tigrinum* was used for limb exchanges with *punctatum* the grafts deviated significantly from their customary growth rates. Later I encountered the same situation when eyes and limbs were grafted from *Amblystoma* to another genus of salamandar [18]. But the most striking and revealing examples of size regulation exerted by the host environment came from the transplantation of other organs, notably the heart, spinal cord, and ear.

When the heart rudiments were exchanged between *punctatum* and *tigrinum,* the grafts at first followed their genetic trends and accordingly became "too large" or "too small" for the hosts they were serving. Instead of continuing in this manner, however, as eyes and limbs would have, they soon began to adjust their size to that of their bearers, and eventually assumed proportions entirely appropriate to the species on which they were growing [19]. Although the mechanism by which this adjustment is effected is not clearly understood, it is undoubtedly a response to the functional demands placed upon the hearts by their hosts. After all, a *punctatum* heart in *tigrinum* is called upon to pump much more blood, and a *tigrinum* heart in *punctatum* considerably less, than would flow through them in their normal settings. It is not surprising that the grafted hearts do not follow the same rules as eyes and limbs, which participate less vitally in the basic functional machinery of the organism and are thus freer to express their growth capacities independently of the scale or requirements of the rest of the animal. Short lengths of embryonic spinal cord grafted from *tigrinum* to *punctatum* behaved like the grafted hearts. Transplanted inner ears (Richardson) also showed some size regulation, although the adjustments were not as complete as those of the heart and spinal cord.

Growth Accommodations and Conflicts

The experiments showed, then, that the eye and limb are more independent in their growth than the heart, spinal cord, or ear, possibly because they are less intricately and critically associated with the rest of the animal. Taking the eye as an example, it is true that this organ is a relatively self-contained and circumscribed entity whose size need not vitally affect its own function or disturb that of neighboring organs. But although this is true of the eye *as a whole*, it is not true of the individual components of the organ. There can be no more intimate and vital structural or functional association than that existing between retina and lens, for example, or between eyeball and ocular muscles. In other words, might there not be, *inside* the eye, growth dependencies quite comparable to those manifested by heart, cord, and ear?

Harrison addressed himself to this question by another of his "simple and original" experiments, in which he constructed composite eyes by uniting the retina of one species with the lens of another [20]. Unlike the situation in which entire eyes are grafted between *punctatum* and *tigrinum,* must not something "give," now that an inherently slow-growing retinal sac is paired with an inherently fast-growing lens rudiment, or vice versa? Harrison found that there were indeed size adjustments, with each partner accommodating its growth to that of the other to form an eye of harmonious proportions. Thus a *tigrinum* lens, in forcing a *punctatum* retinal cup to grow larger than usual, itself falls below its customary growth rate; the result is an organ whose total dimensions, and those of its two components, are intermediate between those of the normal *punctatum* and *tigrinum* structures. This same interplay is, of course, operating when a retina is paired with a lens of its own species, as in normal development or when both are grafted as a unit, but, like many of the relationships that shape an organism, it exposes itself only on surgical confrontation.

The mutual effect between retina and lens is not the only example of growth dependencies provided by the eye. Another striking instance is found in the size adjustment the ocular muscles make to the dimensions of the eyeball [21]. When a *tigrinum* eye vesicle is grafted to a *punctatum* embryo, the muscles developing from host tissue and attaching to the rapidly growing graft become much larger than those associated with the smaller, normal eye on the opposite side of the head. One might be tempted to say that this is merely "functional hypertrophy," that is, that the muscles enlarge simply because they are forced to move a larger, heavier eyeball. But muscular enlargement due to use, such as the enlargement of the human biceps or other muscles in response to work or exercise, involves an increase in the size, not the number, of the individual fibers composing the muscle. I found that fiber size remains unchanged in the muscles attached to grafted *tigrinum* or *punctatum* eyes, and that the increase or decrease in the diameter of muscles is accomplished by a corresponding change in the numbers of the component fibers.

Through its optic nerve, the eye exerts growth effects even on the brain. The fibers constituting this nerve originate from cells of the retina and, on growing inward to the brain, cross to its opposite side, where most of them terminate in the roof of the midbrain or "optic tectum." The extent of cell multiplication in this visual brain center is subject to influence by the invading optic-nerve fibers, as evidencd by the reduced size of the optic tectum on one side when the opposite eye has been excised in young stages, or has been replaced by a smaller transplanted organ. By the same token, the tectum enlarges when the number of invading optic-nerve fibers is increased. One of the less exciting features of my thesis research was the measurement of these effects by tedious counts of nerve cells in sectioned brains of *punctatum* and *tigrinum* larvae between which eyes had been exchanged in embryonic stages [21].

With these examples of size regulation within the eye and its community of associated structures, one might assume that the proportions of other organs are similarly shaped by interactions between their component parts. But the embryologist soon learns that he generalizes at his own peril, and in the present connection one need look no further than the limb to find a marked exception. Although it could hardly be disputed that the foot is an intimate and integral part of the leg, and that it is in the interest of both function and aesthetics that the two be harmoniously proportioned, one of my graduate students at Stanford, Duane Heath [22], found that when the tip of the young *punctatum* limb, at the stage when it is just beginning to grow out as a short, digit-free stalk, is replaced by the corresponding part of a *tigrinum* limb bud, the grafted piece persists in forming a "mitt" that is grotesquely larger than the *punctatum* limb that it adorns. In the reciprocal transplantation, a tiny *punctatum* hand grows on the end of the massive *tigrinum* host appendage.

The ultimate manifestation of nonconformity in growth is a chimera assembled by uniting the anterior half of an embryo of one species to the posterior half of an embryo of another. *Punctatum-tigrinum* graft hybrids like this were first constructed by Stone, and later by one of my own students, Gilbert Church [23]. The front and rear portions of the composite larvae preserve their own independent growth rates to a remarkable degree, with the result that a small head, "shoulders," and forelegs are coupled to huge "hips," hindlegs, and tail; or conversely, a tiny rear-assembly trails behind a massive front half (Fig. 7). In showing that there is no overall, or master, device for forcing the major subdivisions of the body into conventional proportions—a device like those that regulate the proportions of the heart and spinal cord—this experiment is indeed a dramatic revelation of the importance of hereditary autonomy in the control of relative growth.

A Concept of Size Regulation

Can we summarize the factors that regulate proportionate organ size? Rarely, as with the heart, a single factor, say function, might seem to provide the only mechanism needed to insure ultimate size adjustment. More often, however, no such simple situation exists; the problems commonly presented can be illustrated by continuing our reference to the eye. Quite unlike the heart, it is an organ with a strong capacity to express its genetic growth rate independently of the growth intensity of the rest of the animal. It is true, as we have seen, that its total size is partly a product of mutual growth influences between its parts, but this is an adjustment within itself, not an adjustment between it and the organism. Since we have to assume that the growth of the eye *is* geared with that of the body by some sort of coordinating mechanism, can we devise an experiment that will expose its operation?

This was done by exchanging eyes between younger and older salamanders [18, 24]. Transplantation between individuals in different embryonic stages is not adequate for this purpose, since the embryonic period is so brief that one can create only small age differences between the grafts and their recipients.

FIGURE 7. *Chimeras, or graft hybrids, created by uniting anterior and posterior portions of embryos of rapidly and slowly growing species of* Ambly- stoma. *Arrows indicate where the unions were made. The sizes of the two portions of a graft hybrid do not adjust to one another, with the result that the large anterior* tigrinum *portion is combined with rela- tively tiny hindlimbs and tail (left), while the small* punctatum *head and forelimbs are dwarfed by the* tigrinum *body and hindlimbs (right). (From Fig. 1, G. Church, J. Morph., 98:409.)*

Accordingly I turned to the ensuing larval (tadpole) period, in which one can use donors and hosts differing widely in stage of growth. When the eye of an old larva is replaced with an eye from a young one, it can truly be said that the graft is "too small" for the host; and in the reciprocal transfer, from old donor to young host, the graft is unquestionably "too large."

The experiments showed that there must indeed be a mechanism that gears the growth of the part with that of the whole, since normal size relationships between the eyes and their hosts were restored through acceleration or retardation in the subsequent growth of the transplants [18, 25]. In constructing a hypothesis about the nature of the regulatory mechanism, the proposal was made that it is based on progressive changes occurring during larval growth, both in the eye and in the host environment that nourishes it [26]. It was postulated that the changes in the eye itself consist of a gradual decline in the capacity of its cells to assimilate or utilize nutrient materials for growth. Evidence for the existence of this differential is offered by an experiment I later performed at Stanford University in collaboration with a graduate student, Louis DeLanney [27]. Eyes were grafted from young to old larvae as before. Instead of being fed, the hosts were deprived of all food from the time the transplantations were made. Under these conditions the hosts and their own normal eyes were unable to grow, and, in fact, they often shrank appreciably in size. The young transplants, however, achieved a very significant increase in size, demonstrating that young organs are able to extract materials for growth from sources that are subthreshold for their older counterparts.

However, this assimilative advantage associated with physiological youth will not alone account for the observed facts. It explains why the transplant grows faster than the normal organ of the host, but for the graft fully to overcome its initial disadvantage in size, it must not only grow faster than its new mate, it must actually exceed its *own* normal growth rate. At first I believed that this growth acceleration of the young graft might simply reflect the competitive advantage it held over the older host tissues in securing materials for growth from a common blood stream. But this was not borne out by an experiment designed to test it. As we have just seen, young eyes can grow even during the starvation of their older hosts, when competition for any residual food in the blood must be especially keen. What would happen if we make it even more acute? This was done by amputating the tail of the host, so that the young eye was now pitted against a regenerating tail in the postulated struggle for food [27]. Somewhat to my surprise the young grafts grew just as well under these conditions as when the tails were intact, and from this I had to conclude that if competition does not operate under the stringencies of starvation it is hardly likely to do so under the conditions of greater abundance that prevail in animals that are feeding freely.

In seeking alternative reasons that might explain why eyes grow better when grafted to older hosts, I considered the obvious possibility that the blood of older larvae might offer a richer supply of nutrients than is supplied by that of the younger donors. At this point I recognized that my iris shears had led me beyond my depth, and I was fortunately able to enlist the collaboration of a biochemist, W. J. van Wagtendonk, who could help test the hypothesis by making determinations of food content in the blood of *Amblystoma* larvae [28]. Using samples that I took by micropipette directly from the heart, he measured the concentrations of sugar, total nitrogen, nonprotein nitrogen (which includes amino-acid nitrogen), and amino-acid nitrogen itself, in the blood of *tigrinum* larvae of a wide range of ages. The concentration of blood sugar was found to remain remarkably constant throughout larval life, but the nonprotein and amino-acid nitrogen values rose rather spectacularly during the same period. Since amino acids are very important growth requisites, this finding seemed to offer strong substantiation for the idea that organs grafted from younger to older larvae find richer nutrient opportunities in their new environment. One of my graduate students, using quite different chemical methods, was unable to confirm this increase in amino-acid content of the blood with age, but certain features of his findings made it difficult to interpret their significance. There, unfortunately, the matter still stands, but until the problem is reinvestigated, the burden of evidence, both biological and chemical, seems to favor the hypothesis as originally proposed.

On this assumption, let me then present briefly a conception of the manner in which the growth of an organ is geared with that of the rest of the animal [26]. The eye will continue to serve as an example, although the same rules probably hold for other organs and tissues except as they may be influenced by superimposed factors such as function and hormone action. As the eye increases in size and physiological age its cells suffer a gradual loss in assimilative capacity. This is accompanied by a gradual improvement in the nutritive opportunities afforded them by the blood stream. These two sets of changes together provide an effective means of insuring constant size adjustment. The size of the eye at any given moment is a function of its own assimilative capacity and the nutritive opportunities afforded by its environment at that particular stage of growth. Thus in the course of normal development a stage of equilibrium is always in effect. If an eye is placed on an older larva, this equilibrium is disturbed, since the graft is exposed to a richer medium for growth than that to which it was previously adjusted. Growth acceleration ensues, and appropriate size relationships are restored. But this very acceleration speeds the decrease in the graft's assimilative capacity until its growth advantage disappears; that is, the graft's assimilative capacity eventually becomes the same as that of the rest of the animal. At this time, equilibrium is restored.

The problem of how the size of an organ is kept in proper relation to that of the rest of the animal is obviously one that calls for, and might richly reward, further chemical and physiological studies.

In summarizing this investigation of growth, we can say that we are indebted (or can lay the blame) for our bodily proportions to an assortment of unilateral and reciprocal influences operating between part and part, and between part and whole. These influences are difficult to define or describe, and even their classification is difficult. The convenient and seemingly obvious distinction between intrinsic (genetic) and extrinsic (organic environmental) factors tends to fade when we discover, for example, that the "intrinsic" growth rate of the lens is actually an "extrinsic" factor in the growth of the retina. We are also left to wonder why there should be this interplay between lens and retina, and between heart and body, but not between foot and leg, or even between head and trunk. Everything considered, perhaps we should be grateful that we grow up to be as presentable as we are.

II

Berlin Interlude

The growth experiments just recounted, begun at Yale, continued during the first few years after I transferred across the continent to Stanford in 1932. Intercalated between Yale and Stanford, however, was a year of study in Germany. It is this brief association with the Spemann school, along with other considerations mentioned in the Foreword, that I use as justification for the present section of the book.

The "Spemann Story" is principally the story of the discovery and subsequent analysis of the amphibian "organizer," a portion of the embryo that plays a prominent role in directing the development of other important parts of the germ. Definitive proof of its existence was first published in a series of papers between 1918 and 1924, but the inspiration that led eventually to this documentation came from experiments performed much earlier, near the turn of the century.

One of Embryology's Finest Hours

It was Spemann who first performed the classical experiment showing dependency of lens formation on stimulation by the retinal vesicle. Since this was also the first direct demonstration of the existence of an embryonic inductor,

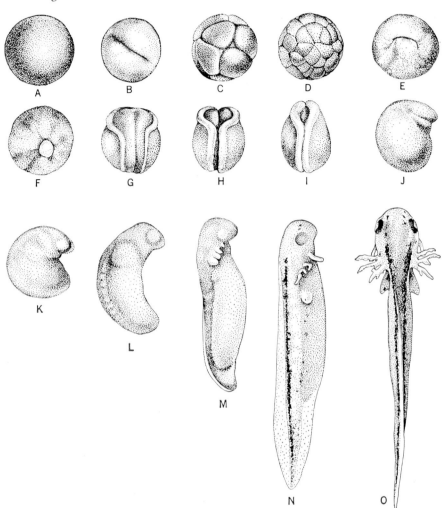

FIGURE 8. *Representative stages in the embryonic development of the salamander Taricha torosa. The egg divides through repeated cleavages (A, B, C, D) until it becomes a hollowed, many-celled sphere. Subsequently (E) a crescentic groove, the blastopore, appears below the equator, and gradually deepens to form a spacious internal cavity as more and more surface tissue moves into the interior at the blastopore. Invagination is well-advanced in F, and when the small plug of tissue occluding the blastopore is finally enveloped an opening is left that will become the anal opening of the digestive tract. The tissue lining the internal cavity formed by this process of gastrulation will form not only the gut epithelium but also the main body musculature and other key dorsal structures such as the notochord, an axial supporting rod that is later*

Spemann was the first embryologist to become aware of the possibility that inductive relationships might be of widespread occurrence in the embryo. Yet it was not alone this experience with the lens that led him to the most important inductor of them all, the so-called "primary organizer," that he discovered later. During roughly the same period in which he was experimenting on the eye, he was also investigating [2] another problem that was receiving much attention in those formative years of experimental embryology: the question of the self-differentiating capacity of the egg, particularly as tested by separating it into two halves to see whether each formed a "half-embryo," or "regulated" to form a whole one. The method Spemann used was to place a loop of hair around the egg and gradually tighten it until the two halves were pinched apart (Fig. 9).

When the two cells formed by the first division of the fertilized egg were separated in this way, Spemann found that both halves of some eggs formed complete embryos, which continued to develop into perfectly normal larvae. With others, however, only one cell formed an embryo, and the second one grew into a spherical or irregular mass that lacked all the cardinal features of embryonic organization. The basis for this difference proved to be in the variable relationship that the first-division plane bears to the future plane of symmetry of the embryo. In some eggs the cleavage cutting them into two cells corresponds closely with the future median plane of the organism; that is, the descendants of one cell will form the right half of the animal, and those of the second will develop into the left half. Eggs in this category give rise to two complete embryos when they are halved at the two-cell stage of development. In other eggs, however, the first cleavage may be at approximately right angles to this plane and divide the egg into a cell destined to form the dorsal half of the embryo and another scheduled to form the ventral half. When two such cells are separated, it is only the "future dorsal" cell that develops into an embryo. Obviously the egg is already partly patterned at a very early stage; the factors essential to normal organization are present in the half of the egg that will form the dorsal part of the embryo—and are therefore represented in both lateral halves—but are lacking in the half that normally develops into the

replaced by the vertebral column. Gastrulation is followed by nerulation (G, H, I), during which the dorsal ectoderm thickens into a horseshoe-shaped plate whose lateral margins move together and fuse in the midline to form the tubular brain and spinal cord. The subsequent drawings (J, K, L, M, N, O) show the gradual emergence of body parts (head; eyes; behind the eyes the rod-shaped organs known as the balancers; gills; limb; fin; skin pigment cells grouped into paired dorsal bands).

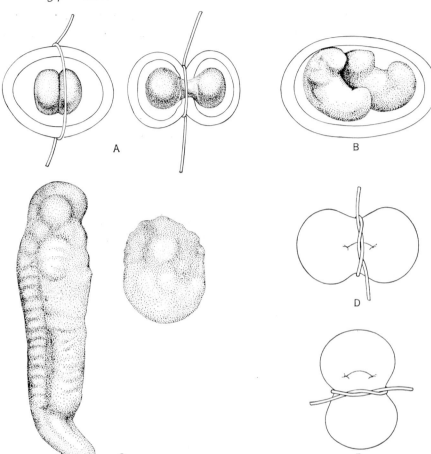

FIGURE 9. A: *Separation of the egg into two cells by constriction in the plane of the first cleavage.* B: *Both cells develop into complete embryos when the first cleavage plane coincides with the future median plane of the embryo.* C: *When the first cleavage plane coincides with the future horizontal plane of the embryo, only the cell destined to form the dorsal half develops into a normal embryo; the second cell forms merely an unorganized cellular mass.* D and E: *Both of these eggs were incompletely constricted in the two-cell stage, and the loops of hair left in position until the blastopores appeared. In D the first-division plane proved to be in the future median plane, since the hair loop bisects the blastopore; if the loop is now drawn tight, each half of the embryo will form a complete organism. In E the first division plane was in the future horizontal plane, since only one half of the embryo contains a blastopore and will accordingly be able to develop normally.* (After H. Spemann, Embryonic Development and Induction, Yale University Press, New Haven, 1938.)

ventral part of the organism. We begin to see that ventral parts, unless associated with dorsal ones, are just as helpless as is the lens epidermis in the absence of its inductors. In the very first years of this century, then, Spemann was already on the track of the primary organizer.

After ligating an egg in the plane of the first-cleavage division, Spemann had to wait for some time before knowing whether he had separated future lateral halves, or dorsal and ventral halves, of that particular embryo. A reliable landmark for making this distinction does not emerge on the surface of the salamander egg until the stage of gastrulation, which is the period in development when the primitive gut cavity is formed. Gastrulation begins with the appearance of a short transverse indentation or groove below the equator on the still-spherical embryo. This groove, called the "blastopore," later deepens and enlarges into a spacious internal cavity lined by tissue that will form not only the digestive tube but also the main body musculature and other key dorsal structures such as the notochord, which is an axial supporting rod that is eventually replaced by the sturdier vertebral column. The movements by which these tissues shift from the surface to the interior of the embryo during gastrulation is a dramatic story in itself, but for our present purposes it is sufficient to say that from the moment the blastoporal groove first appears, the future axes of the embryo can be infallibly predicted. The blastopore will eventually become the anal opening at the posterior end of the trunk, and the vertical plane bisecting the young blastopore and the rest of the embryo will be the median plane separating right and left halves of the organism.

By incomplete constriction of an egg at the two-cell stage, that is, by leaving the two halves joined by a bridge until gastrulation begins, Spemann could tell by the position of the blastopore whether the constriction had been in the future median or in the future horizontal plane (Fig. 9, D, E). If the blastoporal slit spanned the bridge connecting the two halves, he knew that in this particular egg the first-cleavage plane had coincided with the future median plane of the embryo. If the slit formed away from the bridge, in only one of the halves, the first-cleavage plane had been in the future horizontal plane. At this stage he could either remove the ligature and leave the two halves attached, or tighten it further and sever their connection. If the bridge was preserved, the two parts developed either as conjoined twins or into a single embryo with an amorphous mass attached to its belly. If the constriction was completed, the two halves, of course, formed either separate whole twins or one embryo and an unorganized fragment.

Thus Spemann could begin to narrow his search to the portion of the embryo near the young blastopore, although it was actually not until about two decades later, after increasingly refined experiments continued to focus attention on this region, that the culminating and decisive experiment was performed. If the blastoporal area is indeed the source of instructions to other parts, why not graft it to an unaccustomed location in the embryo and see if the surrounding tissues respond to its influence by appropriate modifications of their previously scheduled development. And thus the concept of the organizer was born. The young blastopore and the tissue bordering it were cut out as a unit and implanted in the future belly region of another young gastrula. Here in this alien location, a new embryo developed face to face with its host.

This result did, however, leave one crucial question partly unanswered, namely, whether the grafted blastopore had truly induced the new embryo to form from host cells, or whether the transplant might merely have self-differentiated into the accessory embryo without actually incorporating surrounding host tissue. As pointed out earlier, the healing of embryonic transplants is usually so rapid and perfect that unless special measures are taken one may soon lose track of where graft stops and host begins. Spemann and his student, Hilde Mangold, took such measures: they used donor embryos whose natural pigmentation differed strikingly from that of the hosts [29]. Most amphibian embryos are dark, but one of the European newts lays almost snow-white eggs, and tissue grafted from its embryos to those of other species stands out vividly against the host background (Fig. 10, B). The use of these white embryos as donors of blastoporal transplants showed immediately that both graft and host participate in the formation of the accessory embryos. In brief, the graft does indeed self-differentiate, forming the very structures it would have given rise to in its normal setting; but—and much more important—it also "reworks" as much of the adjoining host tissue as is necessary to round out a complete embryo.

The joint participation of grafted and host tissues in formation of the secondary embryo is shown in cross section in Figure 10, E. Above is the primary or host axis, with its component spinal cord, notochord, and prominent premuscle masses (somites). Renal (kidney) tubules are also seen. Below, we see both grafted and host tissues collaborating harmoniously in forming the same components of the induced secondary axis. The white graft has differentiated into a notochord, and also into somite tissue; in its role as organizer it has converted adjacent host cells into additional somite tissue and kidney tubules, and has induced the overlying belly epidermis to form a spinal cord.

One of the first questions posed by Spemann's discovery was a topographical one, namely, the extent of the area that possesses this remarkable organizing ability. Systematic testing of grafts taken at different distances from the young blastopore established that the area coincides closely with the part of the embryo that moves to the interior during gastrulation and differentiates primarily

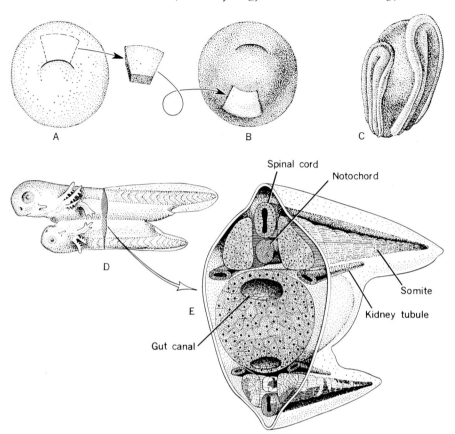

FIGURE 10. *Induction of accessory embryo by transplantation of the organizer. A block of tissue bordering the young blastopore (A) is grafted to a second embryo of the same age, which now has two organizers (B) instead of the usual one. Under the influence of the grafted organizer an extra embryonic axis (C) appears, and develops into an essentially complete embryo joined face to face (D) with the host embryo. Transplantation of the organizer from a white donor embryo to a pigmented host makes it possible to distinguish the parts of the induced embryo that are formed by the grafted organizer from those that arise cooperatively by transformation of host tissues (E). (After V. Hamburger,* A Manual of Experimental Embryology, *University of Chicago Press, Chicago, 1960; and after J. Holtfreter and V. Hamburger in Willier et al,* Analysis of Development, *Saunders, Philadelphia, 1955.)*

into the notochord and somites. This emphasizes again that the organizer is not a disembodied entity: it is first and foremost a corporate and prominent part of the dorsal body axis. In its second and superimposed role, that of inductor, it assures the completion of that axis by causing the overlying ectoderm to form the central nervous system.

A most dramatic and conclusive demonstration of the indispensability of the archenteric roof in promoting differentiation of the nervous system was provided by Holtfreter [32] through interference with the process of gastrulation. Normally, of course, the gastrulation movements carry the mesodern and endoderm *inside* the ectoderm, but under certain experimental conditions the direction of movements can be reversed and the ectoderm is left behind as an empty shell. Early and terminal stages of this process of "exogastrulation" are shown in Figure 11. The ectoderm, deprived of its association with the organizer, is completely unable to form nervous-system tissue or other ectodermal derivatives,

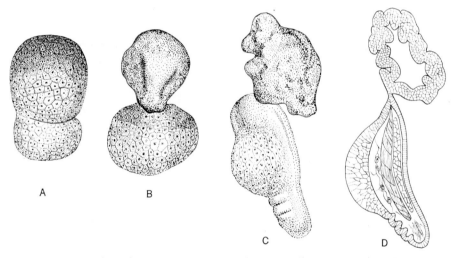

A   B   C   D

FIGURE 11. *When the organizing tissues that normally invaginate to the interior of the embryo during gastrulation are caused to evaginate instead (A), the ectoderm is left as an empty shell (B, C) and is unable to form its normal derivatives, such as the central nervous system, and epidermal structures like the lens and inner ear. The evaginated tissues, however, develop into an embryo-like structure (C, D) possessing many of the cardinal features of normal organization, although lacking skin and all other ectodermal components. (A, B, C after J. Holtfreter, Die totale Exogastrulation, eine Selbstablösung des Ektoderms von Entomesoderm, Arch. EntwMech. Org.,* **129:**669–793, *1933; and D after J. Holtfreter and V. Hamburger in Willier et al, Analysis of Development, Saunders, Philadelphia, 1955.)*

while the evaginated mesoderm and endoderm make an impressive and not entirely unsuccessful effort to form a recognizable embryo. It has no skin or nervous system, of course, and because of the reversed gastrulation it is turned completely inside out; but it possesses a notochord, muscles, renal tubules, and even abortive gill structures in the everted pharyngeal region. Many other experiments could be cited in which predictable abnormalities have been produced by appropriate rearrangements of the organizer tissue; in other words, "as the organizer goes, so goes the embryo."

An Unoriginal Idea

The definitive paper by Spemann and Hilde Mangold on the heteroplastic transplantation of the organizer was published in 1924 [29]. In 1925, my first year at Yale, the annual national meetings of the American Society of Zoologists were held in New Haven during the Christmas holidays. For my labors in vending banquet tickets I was admitted free, and thus heard Dr. Harrison's presidential address in which he mentioned the accelerated activity in embryology caused by Spemann's discovery of the organizer. He referred to the earlier defections of embryologists to the Klondikes of endocrinology and genetics, and noted with gratification the opening up of this new Yukon to which eager miners were now rushing to dig for gold around the blastopore.

These mining activities were still in full swing after I had completed my graduate work and spent two additional years at Yale as an instructor in the Department of Zoology, and I decided that I should widen my research horizons by doing a bit of prospecting myself. At Dr. Harrison's advice I chose to study in the laboratory of Spemann's former student, Dr. Otto Mangold, at the Kaiser Wilhelm Institut in Berlin. I suspect Dr. Harrison may have recommended Berlin, instead of Spemann's laboratory in the more provincial city of Freiburg, because of the cultural enrichment a great European metropolitan center might offer to a product of the American Midwest. Dr. Harrison always seemed to delight in ribbing me gently about my Hoosier background, and especially in reminding me of Indiana's notoriety at that time as a leading stronghold of the Ku Klux Klan. But this hope for my cultural salvation was misplaced: I am afraid that I failed him. Berlin did indeed prove to have its distinctive charms, but it could hardly be said that those I discovered were the ones to be found by haunting the great museums and opera houses.

In my letter to Dr. Mangold requesting the hospitality of his laboratory, I proudly outlined a research program that I was sure would impress him by its originality. After the organizer was discovered one of the crucial questions that arose was whether it not only induced the formation of the basic components of the embryo such as the central nerve tube, but also shaped their distinctive hereditary characteristics as well. This is an aspect of inductive phenomena in which I developed an early interest, undoubtedly because my thesis research on the heteroplastic transplantation of organs focused my attention on the developmental basis of differences between species. One species difference that attracted my notice in particular was the presence or absence of the larval organ known as the "balancer," a rod-shaped structure that grows out just behind each eye, and withers or is lost not long after the hatching of the young larva from its egg capsule. Although characteristic of many salamanders it is absent in others, for example, *Amblystoma tigrinum* and a related species, the Mexican "axolotl." There are fewer clear-cut, qualitative differences of this kind between salamander species than one might imagine, and this seemed an ideal one for the purpose I had in mind. My purpose was to learn whether absence of the balancer reflects hereditary inability of the tissues to form this epidermal structure, or whether the inductive stimuli necessary to elicit a balancer are simply lacking in certain species. This problem, and my proposed attack on it, were blithely outlined in my letter to Dr. Mangold. I was surprised recently to find that Dr. Mangold's reply is still in my files, and in it he expressed full approval of my plan. He liked the project so much, in fact, that he had undertaken and completed it himself during the preceding year! In his characteristic way he listed in *eins, zwei, drei* order his experiments and their results. Needless to say I found other projects to occupy my time during the pleasant and profitable year I spent in his laboratory.

In brief, Mangold found that the axolotl embryo lacked a balancer, not because there is any dearth of balancer-inducing stimuli in this species, but because the axolotl epidermis is unresponsive to them [33]. Prospective belly epidermis taken from a young *Triturus* (newt) embryo and grafted to the head of an axolotl embryo responded by forming a balancer typical of the donor species, while in the reciprocal experiment axolotl ectoderm remained refractory when grafted in substitution of future head epidermis on a *Triturus* host.

Spemann and Oscar Schotté addressed themselves to the same problem by exchanging gastrula ectoderm between more distantly related amphibians, salamanders and frogs. In many frogs there is a v-shaped thickening of the head epidermis called the "sucker." It has a sticky secretion that helps the young tadpole maintain attachment to environmental objects or surfaces. Transplantation showed that this difference between the two major groups of amphibians has its basis in the genetic constitution of frog and salamander epidermis, not in any species-specificity of frog and salamander inductors [2]. Frog hosts induced salamander ectoderm to form balancers in keeping with its hereditary makeup, and salamander hosts elicited suckers from the grafts of frog epidermis (Fig. 12). This undeviating adherence to hereditary constitution was further manifested in the behavior of transplants to the mouth region. Salamander larvae have the true dentine teeth that are typical of most vertebrates, but the jaws of frog tadpoles are adorned instead with horny serrations. When ectoderm was exchanged, it was its hereditary nature that determined the character of the induced mouth armor.

In evaluating these results one must not lose sight of the fact that the induced organs, alien as they are to the hosts, are nevertheless appropriate to the *region* where they develop; and for this the organizer must receive full credit. But if the reacting tissue has such wide latitude that it can form adhesive organs differing as radically as balancer and sucker, or mouth armor as unrelated as bony and horny teeth, then one must concede that the blueprint supplied to the reacting tissues by the organizer outlines only the barest floor plan for its development.

"Chaos Out of Order" (and Back Again?)

Considerations such as these bring us face to face with the question of the chemical or physical nature of organizing action, and the first groping attacks on this enormously difficult and still controversial problem were just getting well under way in Mangold's laboratory during the year I spent there. These early attempts mostly took the form of testing how much and what kinds of abuse the organizer could withstand without losing its touch. It was variously crushed, frozen or heated, and then tested to see whether it could still induce neural differentiation. Holtfreter [34] was the first to achieve signal success by the startling demonstration that heat-killed organizer tissue could indeed elicit nerve-tube formation. I have frequently boasted to my students that "I was there" when he encountered his first clear-cut instance of this phenomenon. I was the only other person working in Mangold's department one spring evening when Holtfreter excitedly invited me into his laboratory to admire a vesicle of young epidermis that was undergoing nerve-tube formation in response to the dead organizer tissue upon which it was lying (Fig. 13). I suspect that Holtfreter, like many biologists following a hot scent, did not ordinarily advertise his findings until they were safely published, usually in *Roux' Archiv für die Entwicklungsmechanik* ("developmental mechanics") *der Organismen*. On this occasion, however, his pride of parenthood could not be contained, and I, in turn, have not failed to seize the opportunity the incident affords me for a bit of embryological name-dropping.

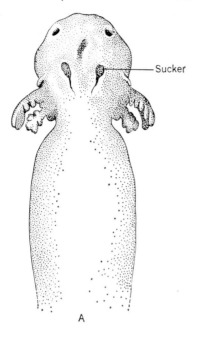

Sucker

A

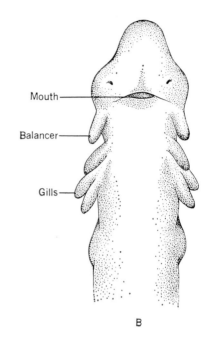

Mouth

Balancer

Gills

B

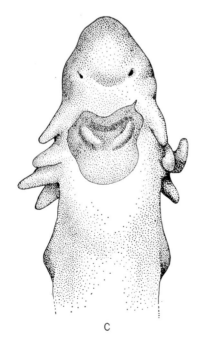

C

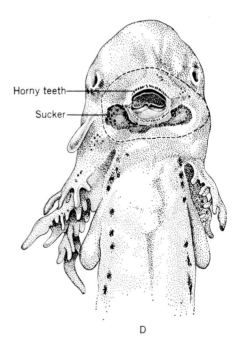

Horny teeth

Sucker

D

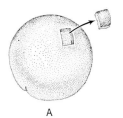 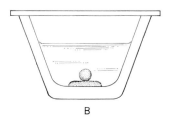 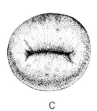

A   B   C

FIGURE 13. A: *A piece of ectoderm is cut out from a young gastrula, and* B: *laid upon a piece of heat-killed organizing tissue in a dish of physiological salt solution.* C: *The explant rounds into a vesicle and then forms a groove which sinks to the interior of the vesicle and forms nerve tissue. (After J. Holtfreter, Nachweis der Induktionsfähigkeit abgetöteter Keimteile, Arch. EntwMech. Org.,* **128**:584–633, *1933.)*

For the next several years similar results followed thick and fast—and confusingly. In fact, many of them were so puzzling and seemingly paradoxical that Holtfreter was to remark despairingly that the analysis of organizer action was rapidly "bringing chaos out of order." It had been surprising enough to learn that a killed organizer could still induce, but it soon proved that other, ordinarily inert, parts of the embryo such as ectoderm became full-fledged neural inductors once they were coagulated by boiling. The roof really fell in when living or killed tissues of adult salamanders, and even from a variety of animals ranging from worms to man, were found to function in this same unexpected way [35]. Nor did efforts to identify the active components of normal and foreign inductors by chemical fractionation serve to reduce the confusion. Separations by Needham indicated that it was the steroid-containing fraction that was active, and this seemed to be supported by positive results

---

FIGURE 12. *Organizers elicit the development of most body parts, but do not control their distinctive hereditary features. This is clear from the results of exchanging future mouth-region epidermis between frog and salamander embryos. The normal salamander larva has true dentine teeth and rod-shaped balancers in this region, while the frog larva has horny epidermal teeth and an adhesive organ called the sucker. (A and B show suckers and balancers, respectively). Frog epidermis grafted to the salamander mouth region persists in forming suckers (C and D), and horny teeth (D). Salamander epidermis grafted to frog hosts forms balancers and dentine teeth. (A, B after V. Hamburger, A Manual of Experimental Embryology, University of Chicago Press, Chicago, 1960; and C, D after H. Spemann, Embryonic Development and Induction, Yale University Press, New Haven, 1938.)*

with chemically pure, synthetic steroids. However, similar claims, equally well supported, were soon made for totally unrelated classes of compounds such as fatty acids and nucleoproteins. One reason why this was so discouraging was that it began to look as if almost any substance could unlock neural differentiation, and if true this would offer no clue to what is happening inside the reacting cells in response to induction.

A finding that at first seemed to be the final blow, but which actually led to some clarification of the confusion, was that gastrula ectoderm could be caused to undergo neural differentiation merely by subjecting it to a mildly toxic medium. This was first reported by Barth [36], of Columbia University, when he isolated ectoderm of *Amblystoma punctatum* in the standard saline solution devised by Holtfreter. The latter found that this was because the medium, although perfectly suitable for tissues of European newt embryos, was too alkaline for isolated *punctatum* ectoderm [37]. Holtfreter then proceeded to show that the supposed inductive effects reported earlier for some of the chemical compounds and even foreign tissues were, in fact, the result of their damage to the ectoderm. Although it has not yet been entirely confirmed, the implication is that inductive substances are widely distributed in the embryo, and that when released through cell damage they are free to induce the differentiation of adjacent cells that have survived the toxicity.

Not all of the inductive effects reported for foreign tissues can be dismissed as the indirect results of cell damage, as more recent work has shown. Of especial interest is the well-established finding that different adult tissues have different inductive actions. For example, alcohol-treated guinea-pig liver induces— almost exclusively—anterior-head structures (fore- and midbrain, for example) of ectodermal origin, while similarly treated bone marrow elicits principally mesodermal structures of the trunk and tail, such as muscle and notochord. One of the questions raised by results of this nature is whether we are dealing with a few or with many different chemical substances. Is there only one compound responsible for the induction of the whole anterior-cranial complex, or is there a "family" of them, each responsible for evoking a single component such as fore- and midbrain, eye, nose, and balancer? Toivonen and his colleagues [38] in Helsinki believe there may be only two, a single anterior-cranial inductor specializing in the induction of neural structures, and a trunk-tail inductor specific for elicitation of mesodermal structures such as notochord, somites, kidney, and limb. They identify the former as a ribonucleoprotein and the latter as a protein lacking the RNA component. They suggest that these two are present in different concentrations along the embryonic axes, and that it is mixtures of them in different proportions that account for the variety and placement of the body components. In support of this concept they cite the results of grafting the two inductors in combination. Whereas guinea-pig liver induces only anterior-cranial structures, and bone marrow only mesodermal parts of the trunk and tail, when pieces of each are grafted simultaneously their joint action evokes a complete sequence of axial structures that include posterior-cranial structures such as hindbrain and ear.

On the basis of these and other results Toivonen proposes that in normal development the body plan emerges as an expression of two agents or influences whose strengths grade off along the major axes of the embryo. One, a "neuralizing" agent, is most potent dorsally and diminishes ventrally. The second, the "mesodermalizing" agent, is strongest posteriorly and weakens toward the head of the embryo. The dorsal location of the neural axis is an expression of the former gradient; and the predominance of mesodermal components such as somites in the trunk and tail is a manifestation of the latter. Some embryologists are critical of this approach to the interpretation of development, but it is significant that several different investigators (Dalcq, Nieuwkoop, Yamada) have arrived independently at theories involving a system of "double gradients."

The attractiveness of such theories is not difficult to understand, since they make it possible to encompass the complexities of embryonic organization within a fairly simple framework. If one postulates that a separate key substance is essential to the induction or differentiation of each tissue and organ in the body, he is left with the problem of how all of these agents become segregated in the right positions in the first place: what organizes the organizers? In other words, one begs the problem, by substituting one dilemma for another. By postulating only two agents, the first graded in concentration or activity along the antero-posterior axis, and the second along the dorso-ventral axis, one can liken the embryo to a grid in which the product of the two differentials would be quantitatively different at each point of intersection. In Toivonen's terms, for example, the low intensity of the mesodermalizing gradient anteriorly, combined with the high value of the neuralizing gradient along the middorsal line, would result in forebrain formation at the extreme anterior end.

A Brief Personal Involvement

I mentioned earlier that I had a brief personal involvement in the organizer saga. This did not come until several years after my sojourn in Germany. It began through my interest in the discovery by Barth and Holtfreter that toxic agents cause ectoderm to undergo neural differentiation. Since in culturing gastrula ectoderm one cannot always eliminate the possibility that its transformation into nerve tissue is attributable to a few damaged cells rather than to specific agents that the experiment may have been designed to test, it seemed desirable to devise methods for studying single isolated cells whose performance would not be subject to the effects of unhealthy neighbors. I was working at the time on the culture of amphibian skin-pigment cells, and eventually developed successful techniques for isolating these cells singly in capillary tubes of very fine bore [39]. Fluid taken from the body cavities of adult newts proved much more suitable than saline solution as a medium for these naked cells. I recalled that in an early experiment Holtfreter had found that pieces of young gastrula ectoderm sometimes differentiated into nerve tissue when placed in the body cavity of tadpoles. This suggestion that body fluid might have inductive powers was a further reason for using it to culture isolated gastrula ectoderm cells. One difficulty encountered was that the single cells did not always remain single very long! By their very nature as cells of the young embryo, they were still in an active state of division. Whether they divided or not, seldom did any of them exhibit behavior worthy of note. As I recall, one or two differentiated into nerve cells, and a few into pigment cells. (Dr. Man Chiang Niu, a former graduate student who was still working with me at Stanford, later obtained more examples of pigmentary differentiation.) In general the dissociated cells were not exciting or even very healthy, and we had almost arrived at the conclusion that the approach was not a promising one. During this period I was beginning the program of field experiments to be described later, and although I had not yet contemplated turning from embryological work, I doubt that I would have devoted much further effort to the culture of dissociated gastrula cells. But before leaving for a prolonged stint at my remotely situated field station, I suggested to Dr. Niu that he try isolating the cells in larger clusters and thus give them the protective advantage that the members of isolated cell groups seem to confer on one another.

On my return about two weeks later I learned that Dr. Niu had found the answer. As an extension of his thesis research, he was isolating pieces of the young neural plate (known to possess inductive capacity) in drops of saline to test their capacity to yield skin-pigment cells. Through inspiration or great good luck he had taken tiny bits of gastrula ectoderm consisting of only a few cells and introduced them into his week-old cultures of the inductor tissue. Instead of remaining as undifferentiated balls or vesicles, as they would have if isolated by themselves, many of them differentiated into unmistakable nerve and pigment cells. Of immediate and obvious import was the fact that the differentiation of these small cell-aggregates had occurred in the absence of physical contact with the inductor explant, and the assumption that they were responding to products in solution was apparently confirmed by differentiation of ectoderm pieces in cell-free medium taken from established cultures of organizer tissue [40].

Dr. Niu, now at Temple University, has continued to press this study with initiative and imagination, and his results have attracted wide interest. His biochemical studies indicate that ribonucleic acid may be the active component released by the inductor tissue, and even raise the possibility that specific RNA's are responsible for the induction of different tissues and organs such as kidney, liver, and thymus. This potential link between the roles of nucleic acids in heredity and development is an exciting prospect, but there is not yet sufficient information or agreement about the chemical basis of induction to warrant any definitive conclusions or predictions. The difficult and even contradictory status of the problem is illustrated by Barth's subsequent finding [41] that gastrula ectoderm cells of the frog can differentiate into nerve and pigment cells in a saline medium that has not been previously "conditioned" by an inductor tissue.

The Uncertain Road Ahead

In attempting to increase our understanding of the organizer we must return to its even more secretive partner, the reacting tissue. It is difficult enough to study inductors chemically, but even more difficult to get inside the responding tissue and see what is happening there without destroying the very processes we are trying to explore. We have already learned that these processes are immensely important, since they, and not the inductive stimuli, govern the entire genetic pattern of the response. This again raises the question of just how much autonomy or resourcefulness does reside in the reacting cells themselves.

One of the most revealing clues to this problem was the discovery that an artificial inductor, such as a piece of kidney or liver, can induce a remarkably highly organized cranial or trunk-tail complex to form from a piece of young gastrula epidermis [42]. An example of the latter is seen in Figure 14, with all of the induced ectodermal and mesodermal components perfectly placed in relation to one another. In cases like this there can hardly be any highly localized point-to-point control of organization by the inductor, since the piece of liver is a uniformly structured mass presumably lacking any pattern that could correspond, even remotely, to that of the complex that it has induced.

This must mean that the instructions given by the inductor are of an extremely general nature, in this example specifying merely "posteriority," and that factors in the reacting ectoderm then take over and themselves establish a

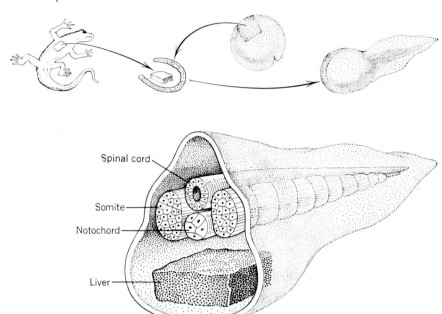

Spinal cord

Somite

Notochord

Liver

FIGURE 14. *A fragment of liver jacketed in a piece of gastrula ectoderm causes the latter to organize itself into a tail with all its component parts arranged in the proper relationships to one another. (After J. Holtfreter, Some aspects of embryonic induction,* Growth **10**:138, 1951.)

pattern of organization. To a greater extent than has been assumed thus far in our discussion, the tendency or capacity for organization is an inborn property of all embryonic tissues, not merely of those that we normally think of as inductors or organizers. Nor should this strike us as odd, if we bear in mind that all cells of the embryo have complete and identical sets of genes, that is, repertories of genetic information, and that the selective expression of this information at different points along the body axes theoretically need not depend upon highly specific inductive agents.

I referred earlier to the work of the Spemann school as "one of embryology's finest hours." Possibly the finest moment of all will come when the basis of induction is resolved in chemical terms. But it should be evident by now that embryonic organization is such a many-faceted phenomenon that no single chemical principle or discovery will encompass all its aspects, and also that the significance and relevance of information gained by the chemist must be tested against the wide background of facts exposed by his surgical forebears.

In turning the problem over to the chemical embryologist let me, as a representative of the organismic school, give him our blessings. The recent advances in chemical genetics have given the molecular biologist a sense of confidence and optimism that may or may not be entirely justified. If genes are nucleic acids, and nucleic acids control protein synthesis, isn't the link between heredity and development already forged and the secret of differentiation largely exposed? I do not doubt that in a limited sense it is, or eventually will be. The cytological differences between lens, muscle, and blood cells reflect principally the differences between their constituent proteins, and the continuing attack on the genetic code is bound to tell us more and more about the sequences of chemical events leading to the differentiation of these and other tissue categories.

Great accomplishments in this area are undoubtedly forthcoming, and the embryologist who remains unelated by them will be a confirmed classicist indeed. It may equally well be said that it is a naive molecular biologist who thinks that his present or immediately foreseeable approaches promise a ready solution to all, or even the most central, problems of development. In claiming this, I am taking the position that the experimental embryologist, although perhaps not as well qualified to lead the chemical attack on these central problems, is nevertheless better equipped than anyone else to define their essential nature.

One of these problems is thrown into bold relief by the experiment just mentioned, in which a piece of liver induced an envelope of gastrula ectoderm to develop into a well-organized trunk-tail complex (Fig. 14). Components of the complex include muscle, skin, notochordal, nervous and connective tissue, and, as already conceded, it may not be long before the chemical ontogeny of each of those cell types is well understood. Let us even assume, for present purposes, that this happy time has already arrived, and that the steps linking nucleic acids and distinctive tissue proteins are known in detail for each of the tissue categories. However, even with all of this information at hand, the features of the experiment that are of greatest interest to the embryologist might be as obscure as ever. These are the facts that the various tissues of the induced complex are *properly placed within an organismic framework,* and that this placement has been worked out within the reacting ectoderm without any possibility of guidance by the inductor itself. That is, the embryologist is more concerned with the factors that localize the activity of different tissue-specific nucleic acids within appropriate areas of the reacting ectoderm than he is with the subsequent chemical elaboration of these tissues. Stated somewhat differently, he is more concerned with *organization* than with *differentiation,* and he will refuse to concede that the molecular biologist is fully "on track" until he encompasses this primary aspect of development in his plan of attack. Since the molecular biologist derives his conceptual approach more from genetics than from embryology, the prospects that he will give high priority to the problem of organization are perhaps doubtful. I sympathize fully with his reluctance to address himself to problems offering so few points of vulnerability as do strictly organismic phenomena such as organization and regulation. In the example just chosen, in which a highly patterned complex emerges from an unpatterned expanse of ectoderm in response to an unpatterned stimulus, neither the concepts of physiological genetics nor the spectacularly successful methods of microbial genetics may be readily applicable. The gene is a unifying concept and unfailing tool in genetics, but less obviously so in embryology [43]. It enables one to understand, or at least investigate, why the notochord of the aforementioned trunk-tail complex is the notochord of a salamander instead of a frog, but we must still inquire why "notochordal genes," of whatever species, are chosen to express themselves in one part of the system and not in another. When the molecular biologist moves into embryology he must be prepared to recognize this problem and attack it, or concede that he is engaging development only at its periphery. Or, refusing the challenge, he must at least be tolerant of the unifying concepts that the embryologist tries to develop for himself. These will inevitably be less atomistic than those of biochemistry or biochemical genetics, and for this reason perhaps less appealing scientifically.

This may be why the most comprehensive single undertaking of this nature, Child's formulation of the concept of physiological gradients, met with so much opposition, even from many fellow biologists. As I implied near the beginning of this book, I was somewhat starry-eyed about Child's writings at the time I entered graduate school; consequently I was unprepared to find his ideas subjected to such scathing criticism as I encountered in the elite scientific circles of the eastern universities. It is possible that Child courted this reaction by his belligerent advocacy of his concept, but even so I doubt that he merited the almost savage thrusts he received from some of his illustrious colleagues. When I knew him at Stanford, where he worked for many years after his retirement from the University of Chicago, he had lost none of his zest or conviction, but he championed his ideas with as much moderation as could be expected of a man who had built most of his scientific career around a single, treasured concept.

In the guest lectures he gave each year in my course in experimental embryology, he loved to point out—always with a mischievous grin in my direction—that the amphibian egg is after all a peculiarly unsuitable object for the study of development! As a loyal devotee of the salamander egg, I naturally rejected this verdict, but at the same time I recognized that his charge served to illustrate a legitimate point. As deliberately overstated by Child, this point is that the amphibian egg is already "organized" at the time it is laid, and that all that remains is its "differentiation." By this he meant that the basic pattern of the organism is already foreshadowed in the egg by localization of the organizing center and body axes, and that much of subsequent development can be regarded as mere fulfillment of this initial plan of organization.

If the main problem of development is to understand how a patterned system evolves from an unpatterned one, then the ideal systems for study are those in which the very first inception of pattern can be investigated. Working mainly with lower invertebrates, Child claimed to show that pattern always emerges in response to external differentials such as oxygen supply, light, or temperature, and consists initially of purely quantitative differences in physiological activity (such as oxygen comsumption and carbon-dioxide production) along the axes of the egg or other developmental unit. Once a quantitative gradient is established in this way, Child argued, local qualitative differences will inevitably arise secondarily and lead to different gene-based morphological expressions along the developmental axes. One of his favorite examples was drawn from the work of my colleague, Douglas Whitaker [44], with the egg of the common brown seaweed, *Fucus*. If placed in a pH gradient, the half of the egg exposed to the more acid sea water always developed into the basal part of the plant, while the cell descendants of the other half formed the main, branching portion of the alga. Other differentials such as light, gravity, and mechanical pressure exerted this same polarizing effect on the egg.

In his writings Child applied his concept—which I dare not develop further in the fear of going hopelessly astray from the salamander trail—to a wide spectrum of organisms and developmental systems [45]. In fact he applied it so universally that he weakened his case; theories that explain everything are sometimes accused of explaining nothing. It cannot be denied, however, that he attempted to strike at the very roots of the phenomenon of development, and I predict that the molecular biologists will eventually have to accept some of his formulations and findings if they are to attack effectively the truly organismic aspects of ontogeny. The recurring resort to gradient concepts by students of the amphibian organizer possibly presages the ultimate vindication of Child's approach.

Time to Go Home

I left Germany in the summer of 1932, about six months before the political event that was to affect the lives of all the Germans I had come to know at the Kaiser Wilhelm Institut. Other Americans at the Institut, with keener noses for history in the making, often attended the giant gatherings exhorted by the Fuehrer, but I never availed myself of this dubious opportunity and for the most part remained blithely unaware of the brewing social and political upheaval. The research that I undertook during the year, on the determination of the initial size of organ rudiments, was never immortalized in print, largely because I learned that Rotmann, a student of Spemann at Freiburg, already had an excellent head start on the problem; eventually he published an illuminating series of articles on the subject.

The year was eminently worthwhile, not only because of the familiarity I gained with new research methods, but especially because of the privilege of close association or at least acquaintance with Professor Richard Goldschmidt, Johannes Holtfreter, Otto Mangold, and others, including Dietrich Bodenstein, who was later to work with me at Stanford for several years. Bodenstein introduced me to his native East Prussia, where we spent a memorable vacation at the remote fishing village of Rossitten on the Baltic coast. During a week's pilgrimage to Freiburg, I had the opportunity to meet Spemann, and also Viktor Hamburger, who has since become a valued friend in this country. Invited to Spemann's home as a dinner guest one evening, I felt particularly gauche when he proudly showed me his complete collection of Goethe, and seemingly expected some intelligent and sympathetic comments from me concerning the greatness of his favorite author. The only Goethe gem in my limited repertory of literary quotations was one that I had heard attributed to him a few weeks earlier, to the effect that "Der der nicht trinken kann soll nicht lieben, und der der nicht lieben kann soll nicht trinken." I sensed that this might not be the sort of erudition that Spemann was probing for, and explained that to my sorrow the door to masterpieces such as Goethe's had been barred to me by the intricacies of literary German.

Wherever I visited it was evident that Harrison's prestige was, if possible, even greater in Germany than in the United States, and my identification as "ein Schüler von Harrison" always meant open sesame. I recall vividly an incident that illustrates the position he occupied there. A young German embryologist, unaware that Harrison was paying Berlin a brief visit, suddenly found himself in the dazzling presence of the great man on approaching the table where Mangold's group lunched daily. He became rigid as if in tetanic shock, then bowed, walleyed and speechless, deeply from the waist. What wonder that many Europeans visiting Yale for the first time were shocked by the easy air of informality that his students sometimes assumed in their relations with "the Chief."

Even Harrison's students would not have been guilty of the lese majesty I witnessed in the Institut office of Professor Correns, famous as one of the three rediscoverers of Mendel's pioneering work in genetics. An American photographer of prominent biologists, known widely and affectionately as "Radio Pete" because of the conspicuous hearing aid he always wore, visited Berlin as part of a European tour designed to enlarge his collection of portraits and give it international scope. I had known him at the Marine Biological Laboratory at Woods Hole, Massachusetts, and he promptly seized upon me as his guide around Berlin and especially through the laboratories of the Institut. Correns was high on his list of projected subjects, and with some trepidation I requested an audience with the great man. The moment I ushered him into Correns' presence, Pete took full command, as if to make it clear that he had, after all, photographed the best of 'em and had long since passed the stage where he was impressed by mere fame. "Now if you'll just stand over there by the window, old boy, and not be nervous . . . ," in the meantime draping his arm familiarly around Correns' shoulder. After a moment of dazed incredulity, Correns responded with a delighted grin, and thereafter was completely at Pete's disposal.

If I have not already strayed too far from salamanders and science, let me mention one other incident that for some reason occupies a firm and treasured place in my recollections of Berlin. Professor Mary Stuart MacDougall of Agnes Scott College, who was older than the other Americans then at the Institut, complained to me one day that as an unescorted woman she was unable to explore Berlin's celebrated night-life, and frankly proposed that she subsidize an evening's tour of some of the better known spots under my guidance. I was delighted to cooperate, and on a fifty-fifty basis we patronized a few more or less notorious clubs I had visited before and even a couple of especially dubious ones I had been warned against. I had feared that Dr. MacDougall might disapprove of what we would encounter; instead, she enjoyed the evening immensely and could not have been less abashed. Her most memorable reaction came after surveying with objective detachment a group of well-endowed young women posing in their full epidermal glory: "Humph, I've seen lots prettier girls in the swimming pool at Agnes Scott College." I have not mentioned publishing this anecdote to Dr. MacDougall, but I know from recent correspondence that she still remembers our "night on the town" with pleasure and I cannot believe she would resent my allusion to it.

The temptation to remain a second year at the Institut was great. With an annual fellowship stipend of eighteen-hundred dollars, my purchasing power was greater than it has been since, and I was just beginning to get a reasonably firm grasp of the language. But word kept filtering through that the academic marketplace at home was beginning to feel the effects of the depression, and I have since congratulated myself often on my good luck in receiving an offer to teach at Stanford University and my foresight in accepting it. In addition to being a delightful place to live, northern California offers an asset that is perhaps less well known to the millions who have been flocking there in recent years: In my somewhat prejudiced opinion, its newts are unrivalled anywhere in the world!

III

The Newts of California

When I arrived at Stanford in September, 1932, I had no acquaintance with western amphibians and was prepared for the possibility that continuation of my work might depend largely on the good offices of eastern embryologists in shipping me *Amblystoma* eggs each spring. Embryonic surgery was still virtually unrepresented in the west, although Professor J. Frank Daniel and his students, including Richard Eakin and Mandel Schechtman, were beginning to use eggs of the newt, *Triturus torosus,* for analytical study and experimentation at the University of California at Berkeley. My personal introduction to this animal was made by a Yale friend, Homer Violette, who had come to Stanford a year or two before to teach in the Medical School. After the early winter rains had transformed the brown countryside into something less alien to my experience and tastes, Violette took me to ponds high in the nearby Los Trancos Woods where he had found newts breeding the year before. On the few occasions that I had collected *Amblystoma* eggs near New Haven (at Osborn Laboratory this chore was the jealously guarded prerogative of Carl Antonsen, the sometimes tyrannical but much-liked head custodian) we were lucky to bring back two or three dozen clusters. Like the native Californian it is, *Triturus torosus* operates on a more bounteous, ostentatious scale, and I was greatly impressed to see areas of the pond floor almost solidly carpeted by the spherical jelly masses in which the eggs are deposited (Fig. 15).

FIGURE 15. *Photographs showing the abundance in which* torosus *deposits its spherical egg clusters, either directly on the floor of the pond or attached to objects in the water. Each cluster contains about a score of eggs. Photographs taken by Professor C. M. Child on one of his many field trips with the author.*

Prolific and Poisonous

I was soon to learn one reason why the California newt is such a successful, abundant animal. I was still interested in the growth of grafted organs, and when I received a shipment of *Amblystoma tigrinum* embryos from the east, a graduate student, Aubrey Elliott, and I began exchanging eye and limb rudiments between them and *Triturus* embryos. The grafts took successfully and the hosts developed normally, except that when the *tigrinum* larvae reached the stage when they should have begun to swim we were puzzled to observe that they remained motionless, as if under anaesthesia. Eventually they "came alive" before reaching the stage at which feeding begins, but it was clear that something had gone awry and that some effect of the grafted newt tissues must have been the cause [18]. This was confirmed by grinding up newt embryos in salt solution and injecting the filtered extract into the body cavities of *tigrinum* larvae that we had reared to a substantial size. Almost immediate paralysis was the result, followed in an hour or two by complete recovery as the toxin was metabolized or excreted. For the next few weeks no animal that came within our reach was safe; we found that all of the vertebrate animals tested—salamanders, frogs, toads, turtles, and mice—were highly susceptible to the paralyzing effects of the poison. Not all recovered as readily as did the *tigrinum* larvae, and unless the dosage was extremely small, mice developed convulsions that were fatal.

Although the phenomenon was more strictly pharmacological than embryological, it was too intriguing to ignore and at intervals during the next few years I explored several of its aspects in detail [46]. The toxin seemed to be associated primarily with the yolky components of the embryo, since extracts of all yolk-containing stages, from ovarian eggs to newly hatched larvae, were equally potent when tested, whereas extracts of larvae that had completed resorption of their yolk reserves had little or no effect when injected into *Amblystoma* larvae. The toxin proved to be present in the embryos of all the species of California *Triturus,* in approximately the same amounts. It was more weakly represented in embryos of the Japanese *Triturus pyrrhogaster,* and in barely demonstrable form in embryos of the newt of the eastern United States, *Triturus viridescens.* Whereas an eye vesicle or other small embryo fragment of any of the California newts caused prolonged paralysis when grafted to an *Amblystoma* embryo, parabiotic fusion with whole embryos of *pyrrhogaster* and *viridescens* was required to immobilize the *Amblystoma* twins, even for short periods.

The adaptability of embryonic surgery as a technique for biological study was illustrated when it provided kinds of clues and information about the toxin that would ordinarily be sought only by chemical and pharmacological methods. One of these clues was the demonstration that the toxin acted on the motor nerves, but not the sensory nerves of *Amblystoma.* The sensory nerves of the vertebrate nervous system attach to the dorsal half of the spinal cord, and the motor nerves that supply the muscles originate from its ventral half. If the dorsal, sensory half of the embryonic *Triturus* cord was replaced by that of *Amblystoma,* the sensory nerves growing out to the *Triturus* skin from the *Amblystoma* graft were not affected by the massive dosage of host toxin to which they must have been exposed: sensory stimulation of the skin elicited normal muscular contractions. If, instead, the ventral half of the *Triturus* cord

was replaced by a ventral half from *Amblystoma,* the host was completely
paralyzed when it reached the stage at which an embryo normally becomes
motile. It was shown further that *Amblystoma* muscles were unaffected by the
toxin if they were innervated by *Triturus* nerves.

Other grafting experiments pointed to a characteristic of the toxin, its relatively small molecular size, that was later to be confirmed by chemical isolation
and identification of the substance. These experiments were studies of the
mode and speed of transmission of the toxin. Although the circulatory system
is the obvious route by which the toxin travels from the graft to the host nerves
under ordinary circumstances, certain observations suggested that the poison is
also able to reach its target by simple diffusion through the host tissues. This
was confirmed by using *Amblystoma* hosts that had been deprived of circulatory flow through removal of the embryonic heart rudiment. After a "heartless"
embryo had reached the motile stage and begun to swim, it was held quiescent
in a tight-fitting depression in a wax-bottomed operating dish while an eye
vesicle of *Triturus* was grafted low on its flank. Within as little as fifteen
minutes, well before healing of the graft was completed, the host became completely paralyzed. Since there was no arterial-venous circuit for the toxin's
transmission, and since lymphatic flow is not established in salamander larvae
until a later period of development, the toxin was obviously moving by diffusion, and at a rate that seemed to preclude a large molecular size. The same
experiment also gave some indication of the almost incredibly high potency
of the toxin, since, during the short period between application of the graft
and the onset of paralysis, the tiny eye-vesicle could have released only very
minute amounts of the poison.

An even more dramatic indication of the diffusibility and high potency of
the toxin was provided by grafting *Triturus* eye-vesicles to *Amblystoma* hosts
joined in parabiosis. The two embryos were fused tail-to-tail, as shown in Figure
16, and after their hearts were removed a *Triturus* eye was grafted to the

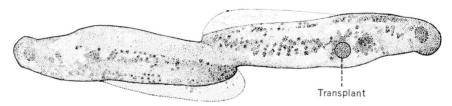

Transplant

FIGURE 16. *Two embryos of* Amblystoma tigrinum *were fused tail-to-tail, and
their blood circulation eliminated by surgical removal of their hearts.
When later an eye was grafted to one twin from an embryo of*
torosus, *the neurotoxin diffusing from the graft soon paralyzed both
twins. After Twitty* [46].

forelimb region of one of them. This twin became paralyzed within a few minutes, and about three hours later enough toxin had reached the second embryo, through the small connecting bridge of tissue, to immobilize it also.

Attempts at chemical isolation and identification of the toxin were made by a colleague, E. L. Tatum, whose work at Stanford with G. W. Beadle on the chemical nature of gene action was later to bring them Nobel Prize awards. Although pure preparations were not obtained, highly concentrated ones were: one gram contained enough toxin to kill an estimated seventy thousand mice. Beyond establishing the important points that the poison is neither a protein nor an alkaloid, and that its molecular size is indeed relatively small, these early efforts led to no positive conclusions concerning the toxin's chemical identity.

AN ODD EVOLUTIONARY COINCIDENCE

Recently, however, the toxin has been the subject of renewed and highly fruitful studies by two Stanford scientists, Harry Mosher, Professor of Organic Chemistry, and Fred Fuhrman, Professor of Experimental Medicine. They have not only worked out its chemical structure but also established the remarkable fact that it is apparently the same poison long known to be present in the ovaries and certain other tissues of the Japanese puffer fishes! [47] In Japan the many human fatalities resulting from the consumption of puffer fish stimulated isolation and study of the toxin, and when Mosher compared purified samples given him by Japanese chemists with his own preparations of newt toxin, he concluded that the two were identical in chemical structure and physiological action. Professors Mosher and Fuhrman have screened many other animal species for the possible presence of the neurotoxin, but thus far they have found it only in puffer fishes and newts. The independent appearance of such a distinctive compound in two groups of organisms as unrelated as puffer fishes and newts is a remarkable evolutionary coincidence, and the results of further comparative studies are sure to be of interest.

Using Tatum's measure of a "mouse unit" as the amount required to kill a mouse weighing twenty grams in ten minutes, Mosher and Fuhrman estimate that one gram of their pure crystalline toxin contains seven million mouse units, which makes it many more times poisonous than cyanide, for example, and one of the most potent of all nonprotein toxins. Dr. Fuhrman characterizes it pharmacologically as an extremely strong local anaesthetic, about 160,000 times as powerful as cocaine. He believes it may prove to be a very useful tool for the study of fundamental neurophysiological problems, including the nature of nervous conductivity.

TOXINS IN ADULT NEWTS

The skin of adult newts of certain species has long been known to contain poisonous secretions, and early in my studies of the embryo toxin I also tested simple aqueous extracts of crushed *Triturus* skin by injecting them into *Amblystoma* larvae. The extracts were indeed toxic, but the physiological effects were quite different from those produced by the embryo toxin. The latter causes paralysis of *Amblystoma* without any significant effect on the heart action, while the skin toxin was found to be primarily a cardiac poison [46]. When administered in strong concentrations it caused complete and permanent heart stoppage; in more limited doses it depressed the pulse rate strikingly without causing marked effects on the motility of the *Amblystoma* larvae. In their tests with mice, Mosher and Fuhrman make no distinction between the toxins found in the embryonic and adult tissues of California newts, but the undeniable difference in the effects produced by these two when injected into *Amblystoma* larvae suggests that further comparisons may be profitable.

In any event, California newts are well armed with poisons, in both embry-onic and adult stages of the life history, and it is not likely that this feature has endeared them to predators. However, there is some conflict of evidence and opinion as to the amount of protection these poisons afford, and also about their effects on the predators. Mosher and Fuhrman cite a report that eastern snakes, when offered western newts, ate them with fatal consequences, but that western snakes refused to accept them as food. I have heard unconfirmed reports from dog owners that their pets have been poisoned by eating newts. But on the other hand, I knew a Stanford student who won a twenty-five dollar wager from his fraternity brothers by swallowing—and retaining—an adult *Triturus,* during the era when ingestion of live gold fish was a popular student pastime. A friend of mine, one of those rare trout fishermen whose word I trust implicitly, tells me he found newts in the stomachs of trout caught in a Siskiyou Mountain lake. And, lamentably, "water dogs" have recently become an in-creasingly popular bait among black-bass fishermen. Oscar Anderson, who assists me in my work with newts, has maintained captive western garter snakes for several months primarily on a diet of adult California newts. He has evi-dence that this is not a totally unnatural diet: on a few occasions he has seen garter snakes regurgitate partly digested newts in response to handling at the time of capture. At my field station in Sonoma County my assistants and I have watched as garter snakes have brazenly stolen newts from containers in which we had stored them temporarily.

None of this means, of course, that snakes or other predators are actually immune to the newt poisons, and I am sure that they would promptly succumb to skin extracts injected directly into their blood streams. Mosher and Fuhrman report that the embryo poison is very much less effective when administered orally to mice, and I found many years ago that this was also true when *Amblystoma* larvae were fed newly hatched *Triturus* embryos.

Whatever the sources of their protection—and it is highly probable that the toxins are one of them—we know that California newts have a low rate of adult mortality. At the time this book is being written, series of animals first marked in 1953, in connection with the study of their homing behavior, are still being captured each year in remarkably high percentages.

New Species Are Born

I have referred in the plural to the species of California newts, but at the time I came to Stanford only one species, *Triturus torosus,* was recognized. My first inkling that there was need for some taxonomic "splitting" came near the end of my first year there. One of the problems confronting those who experiment with amphibian eggs is the short breeding season of most species, and in early June, well after the local spawning season was over, a student and I set out to investigate a report in Tracy Storer's *Synopsis of California Amphibia* [48] that *Triturus* collected at about that time of year in Mendocino County had deposited a few eggs after being brought back to the laboratory. The exact location northwest of Ukiah (see map, Fig. 20) was not specified, but we located a mountain brook about twenty miles from Ukiah in that general direction, and after considerable searching did indeed find a few clusters of embryos.

To our faint surprise the clusters were attached to the undersurfaces of stones, a situation in which I had never seen them deposited in streams near Stanford, and the clusters were also more flattened than the spherical ones I was familiar with. However, I attributed no great significance to these features, and since the embryos were already too far developed for surgical use I paid them no further attention until they hatched some time later. A somewhat idle inspection, preparatory to discarding them, revealed at once that they were strikingly different from the *torosus* larvae I had been working with throughout the winter and spring. The most glaring difference, perhaps, was the color pattern of the hatchlings. The young larvae of all other newt species of my acquaintance show some degree of banding in the arrangement of the brown or black pigment cells (melanophores) present in their skin. Of all species, *torosus* is the most conspicuously banded (Fig. 17). The melanophores, instead of being divided into two pairs of bands, are almost all concentrated into a single, sharply delimited pair of dorsal stripes that persist throughout larval life.

The pigmentation of the Ukiah larvae presented almost the sharpest imaginable contrast to the pattern characteristic of *torosus;* from the moment they first became visible in the skin the melanophores blanketed the entire back and sides evenly and uniformly, without any trace of the banding that characterizes the hatchlings of other newt species. (I may forestall questions arising in readers' minds by saying that the discovery of this marked difference in the larval pigment patterns of *torosus* and the Ukiah species was to set the stage for most of my embryological research during the next several years. For the present we can more profitably continue with the taxonomic sleuthing triggered by the Ukiah expedition.)

The pigmentation was not the only characteristic that distinguished the Ukiah larvae from those I had seen before. They were bulkier, that is, more heavily yolked, and they exhibited two other features that are quite uncharacteristic of newts in general. The dorsal fin, instead of extending anteriorly almost to the base of the head, was absent on the anterior part of the trunk; and the transient larval organ we encountered earlier, the balancer, was either absent or present in stunted, vestigial size (Fig. 18). It is of more than passing interest that absence of the trunk fin and balancer are characteristics that have been noted repeatedly in widely unrelated species that have become adapted to a mountain-brook habitat [49]. It would appear that the Ukiah newts are marching down this evolutionary road.

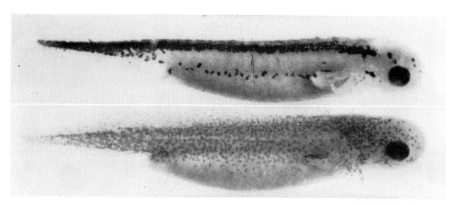

FIGURE 17. *Photographs showing the sharply contrasting pigmentation of the larvae of* torosus *(top) and of the new species discovered near Ukiah, California. (See map, Fig. 20.)*

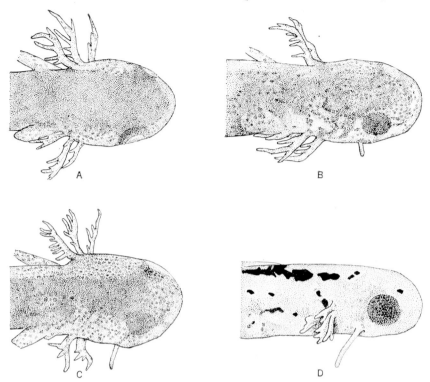

FIGURE 18. *The balancer, which is fully developed in the other forms of California newts* (D), *is either absent* (A) *or vestigial* (B *and* C) *in the new species discovered at Ukiah.*

A year later we visited the same Mendocino County stream and collected not only more embryos but a large sample of adults. This time, of course, we paid close attention to the latter, since it was natural to expect that animals with such distinctive embryos would themselves be different from the adults near Stanford. So they proved to be, although not so strikingly that we would necessarily have noted the differences if we had not been looking for them. The eyes protruded less prominently, the skin was somewhat rougher, and there were reasonably well-defined differences in body coloration; later we were to note also that the arrangement of the two rows of palatine teeth in the roof of the mouth differed significantly, However, the adult differences were by no means as striking as those distinguishing the larvae, and I was not greatly surprised that they had failed to catch the attention of taxonomists who made earlier collections in this general area of California.

The following autumn I began to prepare a manuscript giving a preliminary description of the larvae and adults of this new species of newt. Fortunately I was slothful about completing it, for before the next breeding season was over I was to realize that I was dealing not with one new species, but two. Having collected the Ukiah adults and embryos from the same stream, on the same trip, we assumed that the former were the parents of the latter. But it turned out that we had arrived at the stream too late in the season to encounter the true parents, who had deposited their spawn and left the stream for their underground summer retreats. They were intercepted, this time in the act of laying their flattened egg clusters (Fig. 19) under stones, when we visited streams closer to Ukiah in April of the next breeding season. These handsome animals, which have become my favorites among the California newts, were as distinctive in appearance as their unusual larval offspring. The dark eyes, completely lacking the silvery iris pigment characteristic of other newts, offered a quick and infallible means of identification, and the delicate red of their undersurfaces combined with the almost black pigment on their backs and sides to form a highly attractive body coloration.

But what of the adults found on the earlier trips to Ukiah, and now dis-possessed of the offspring at first assumed to be theirs? The pieces of the puzzle soon fell into place when we brought some of these adults back to the labora-tory and induced them to spawn by use of pituitary hormone. The eggs were smaller even than those of *torosus*, and tiny in comparison with those of the other new Ukiah species; they differed also from those of the other two forms in being deposited singly instead of in clusters; and when they hatched, the pigment pattern of the young larvae set them apart even further from other California newts.

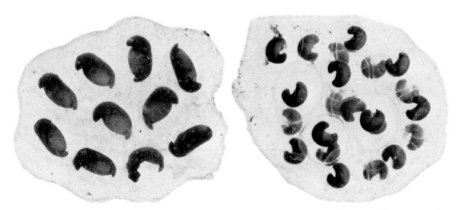

FIGURE 19. *The eggs of the new Ukiah species (left) are deposited in a single-layered cluster, instead of a spherical cluster as those of* torosus *(right) are.*

THE CHRISTENING

The time now seemed ripe for the formal christening of the two Ukiah forms as new species, and this required the choice of names that would do them proper credit. I suppose I might have elected *"melanops"* for the dark-eyed species, but in view of its obvious adaptation and commitment to a mountain-brook setting, *"rivularis"* seemed a more meaningful appellation [50, 51]. The second species presented a more difficult problem, since it exhibited no highly distinctive traits that were readily translatable into a suitable name. However, one of the things that impressed me about the adults of this species was their rather close superficial resemblance to *torosus*. Once one looked for the differences, or had them pointed out to him, they were actually quite clear-cut. Otherwise they could readily escape notice, as indeed they had, notably in the San Francisco Bay area where herpetologists had long encountered both species without differentiating between them. In recognition of its long history of deception, I dubbed this species *"similans"* [51].

By this time Dietrich Bodenstein* had arrived from Germany to work with me at Stanford, and there followed a pleasant mixture of experimental embryology and natural history as we used these species for grafting studies and explored the countryside to learn more about their habits and distribution. We became acquainted with out-of-the-way side roads, ponds, and streams, especially in the Bay area and in the vicinity of Ukiah, that otherwise we would never have had the excuse or occasion to visit. We were baptized in the cold waters of several counties, as we searched the slippery shorelines of rain-filled ponds or clambered along the rocky beds of swift-moving creeks. (But, to borrow a quotation, we always felt rewarded after "getting out of those wet clothes into a dry martini.") We established friendly bonds with skeptical but tolerant motel keepers and filling-station attendants who had never before suspected that "water dogs were good for anything." On one feature of newt biology, however, they were in firm agreement: "If you see them crawling uphill, you know it's going to rain." I was also informed more than once that, according to the news-

---

* Partnership with the volatile and talented Bodenstein, now a noted student of insect development, was sometimes a bit perplexing but most certainly never dull. During the first couple of years after arriving from Germany his facility with English had not yet reached its present high level, and a recent perusal of some of our old research notes confirmed my recollection that they were indeed recorded in a weird—but, oddly enough, still understandable—blend of our two native languages. We developed a remarkable ability to grasp the other's meaning, no matter how expressed. For example, when Bodenstein, an insatiable movie fan, arrived at the laboratory one morning expostulating, "T-vitty, I saw a vunderful moofie last night, Revolt on the Schiff," I knew at once that he had seen *Mutiny on the Bounty*.

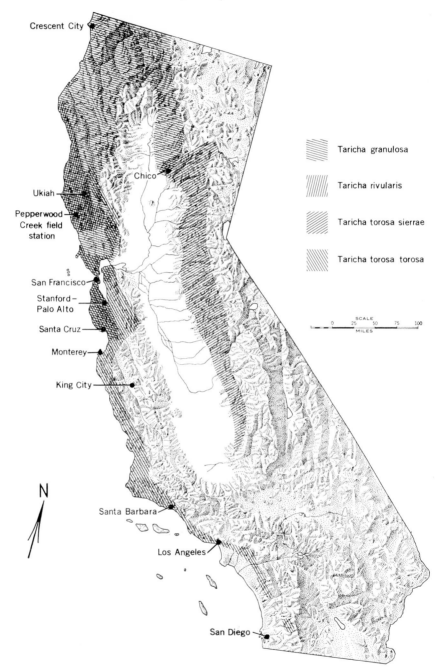

Crescent City

Chico

Ukiah

Pepperwood
Creek field
station

San Francisco

Stanford –
Palo Alto

Santa Cruz

Monterey

King City

Santa Barbara

Los Angeles

San Diego

Taricha granulosa

Taricha rivularis

Taricha torosa sierrae

Taricha torosa torosa

SCALE
0   25   50   75   100
MILES

N

FIGURE 20. *Map of California showing the approximate distributions of the
species and subspecies of* Taricha *and several of the localities referred*

paper, a professor at some college or other had recently found that newts and their eggs were terribly poisonous. They usually added their own documentation of newt toxicity by relating a story that was widely current at the time. It seems that a family (the size of which expanded with each recital of the story) was found dead in an isolated mountain cabin, and on examination of the premises a water dog (or four of five) was found in the teakettle the family regularly filled from a nearby spring. We were never able to trace this story to its source, and although I have not yet been tempted to test its plausibility by quaffing an extract of boiled newts, I can testify with certainty, having often quenched my thirst from newt-filled streams, that *unboiled* newts do not poison the waters they inhabit.

Additional evidence of evolutionary diversification in California newts gradually came to light. Dr. Vesta Holt of Chico State College, who had taken her degree at Stanford under the direction of Professor Douglas Whitaker, sent me *Triturus* egg clusters that she had collected from a stream in the Sierra Nevada foothills near Chico. The large size of the eggs immediately distinguished them from those of Bay Area *torosus,* and the spherical shape of the clusters showed that they had not been deposited by *rivularis.* As they developed to the hatching stage the larval pigment pattern confirmed that Chico *Triturus* was indeed a fourth member of the family group. For a look at the adults, Dr. George Myers of the Stanford Natural History Museum, and I drove to Chico a year or two later and Dr. Holt guided us to Cherokee Creek east of this Sacramento Valley city. Both in appearance and habits the adults were distinctly different from the other species, and in some respects were intermediate between *torosus* and *rivularis.* I gave them full species rank [52], naming them *Triturus sierrae,* but they have since been reduced to the status of a subspecies of *torosus,* by a leading western herpetologist, Professor Robert Stebbins [53] of the Museum of Vertebrate Zoology at Berkeley.

At about the same time, material collected near Monterey and King City, or shipped to me from more southern parts of the state, showed that coastal *torosus* from Monterey County southward was different from that elsewhere. The distinguishing characters, although clearly genetically based, were not of a nature that lent themselves readily to systematic diagnosis and the newts of this region have never been accorded separate taxonomic status.

The most widely distributed species of all, *similans,* has also developed

to in this book. (*Basic map prepared by California Insect Survey, Department of Entomology and Parasitology, University of California; data on distribution of species of* Taricha *from W. J. Riemer, Variation and systematic relationships within the salamander genus* Taricha, Univ. Calif. Publ. Zool., **56**:301–390, 1958.)

geographic variants, but at present only one of these is considered to be sufficiently distinctive to merit recognition as a subspecies. This is a population restricted to Crater Lake in Oregon. The existence of this type first came to my attention when I received adult specimens from the ranger-naturalist at Crater Lake. Alone among western newts, it showed extensive suffusion of the dark dorsal pigmentation onto the ventral body surface. George Myers [54] later applied the Indian name of the prehistoric volcano on whose remnants Crater Lake is located, Mazama, to this interesting, remarkably isolated race.* But I must confess that the subspecies is associated in my mind principally with an unsuccessful trip that Bodenstein and I made to Crater Lake in search of *mazamae* in larval stages. On the return trip our ancient automobile broke down on a desolate stretch of coastal highway south of Crescent City. During a miserable night in the car, and a barely more tolerable three days in the densely fog-bound village of Trinidad, spent waiting for new car parts, our devotion to newts dipped to an all-time low.

The late Sherman Bishop [55] described two or three other geographical variants of *similans* as subspecies, including one from the San Francisco Bay area with the enviable and euphonious name of *twittyi*, but these, alas, have not survived the tests of time and more rigorous systematic appraisal.

THE RECHRISTENING

Readers familiar with western newts will have noted some discrepancies between current nomenclature and the names I have thus far used in referring to the animals. A few years following my recognition and description of *similans* as a separate species, it was established by Fitch that the only newts in Oregon were of this species. Since a newt from the Willamette Valley had been given the name *Salamandra granulosa* by Skilton in 1849, the laws of priority required that *granulosa* replace *similans* as the name of this widely distributed species. (This is, in fact, a good name for another reason: the roughness of the skin caused by the many minute glandular protuberances is usually more pronounced in *granulosa* than in the other species.) Later, when systematists rightly decided that the newts of the western United States deserved recognition as a separate genus, they were removed from the large, inclusive genus, *Triturus*, and designated as *Taricha* [56], a name that had been attached temporarily to specimens collected in the San Francisco Bay area about 1850.

---

* Geologists are apparently in agreement that the crater occupied by this lake was formed by an eruption not more than about 7000 years ago, and it is anyone's guess how long after this *mazamae* emerged as a new and distinct form of *granulosa*.

Taricha succeeds not only *Triturus* but earlier generic names such as *Notopthal-mus* and *Diemictylus*. Where the succession will end no one knows, although *Taricha* now seems well entrenched. Like many biologists I deplore the confusion that results from discarding old, familiar names, but since taxonomists must often name and describe species and genera without complete information about their relationships and distribution, there is scant prospect of escaping this nuisance. It took me some time to learn to say *Taricha*, and the use of

FIGURE 21. *Adult females of* Taricha rivularis (top photo), T. t. torosa (middle), *and* T. granulosa (bottom). *Note especially the rougher texture of the skin and the smaller eyes of* granulosa, *and the black iris of* rivularis (*one of the features distinguishing this species from the other forms of* Taricha).

Triturus in the preceding part of this account has been a pleasant nostalgic indulgence.

There are thus three undisputed species of western newts, with one of them, *torosa* and *granulosa*, each comprising an additional subspecies:

Taricha rivularis—Coastal mountains north of San Francisco Bay (Sonoma, Mendocino, and Humboldt Counties and western Lake County).
Taricha torosa torosa—California coastal ranges from Mendocino County southward to San Diego.
Taricha torosa sierrae—Foothills and western slope of the Sierra Nevada.
Taricha granulosa granulosa—From Alaska south to Santa Cruz County in California.
Taricha granulosa mazamae—From Crater Lake in Oregon.

In the remainder of the book it will be less cumbersome, and undoubtedly less confusing to the reader, if I refer to *Taricha torosa torosa* as *torosa,* and to its subspecies *Taricha torosa sierrae* as *sierrae,* instead of following the more conventional practice of using both specific and subspecific names (or, the abbreviated forms, *t. torosa* and *t. sierrae*) in designating the two geographical races of the species.

The Genealogy of Taricha

No one can be insensitive to the drama of evolution—even of salamanders!—and at least a few things seem clear about the source and relationships of the western newts that now occupy the vast coastal stretch from Alaska almost to the Mexican border. It is pretty well agreed that the ancestors of *Taricha* are of oriental origin, and migrated here across a land bridge formerly linking Asia to North America in the Bering Straits region. These early invaders were probably *granulosa*-like, since this species shares with Asiatic newts certain features such as the arrangement of the palatine teeth, the habit of laying eggs singly, and the pattern of larval pigmentation.

This ancestral *granulosa* apparently underwent no major change until it spread to the more southern reaches of its present range, where eventually *torosa* and *rivularis* emerged as offshoots. Riemer, in his excellent "Variation and Systematic Relationships within the Salamander Genus Taricha" [57], speculates that during the Pleistocene, when the coast ranges were being uplifted, a southern part of the *granulosa* (or *granulosa*-like) population became isolated by the Salinas Trough, which connected the Pacific Ocean with the extensive inland sea occupying what is now the central valley of California. "Differentiation ensued, which included a physiological shift manifested as preference for warmer and more arid situations. With subsequent elimination of the barrier, the southern population, now *torosa*-like, expanded northward to occupy sympatrically part of the range of *granulosa*. During times more favorable than those existing today, *torosa* dispersed around the end of the great central valley to invade the Sierra Nevada. Present evidence does not indicate whether this invasion was from the northern or the southern end of that mountain mass. Subsequent isolation of the Sierra population has permitted differentiation."

I am inclined to believe that the invasion of the Sierra came from the south, partly on the basis of a similarity in the larval pigmentation of *sierrae* and the *torosa* of southern California. In young larvae of northern *torosa* virtually all of the melanophores are restricted to the paired dorsal bands, whereas in both southern *torosa* and *sierrae*, melanophores are not only more numerous on the flanks but are distributed farther ventrally (Fig. 22).

Riemer remarks that it is not clear just where or how differentiation took place between *rivularis* and *torosa*. Perhaps larval pigmentation again provides a clue. As just mentioned, the number and distribution of flank melanophores is different in larvae of northern and southern *torosa*. Until recently the only southern material I had examined came from locations near Monterey, King City, Los Angeles, and San Diego [52]. Since the pigmentation was essentially identical in the larvae from these widely scattered and representative areas, I assumed it was typical of the entire *torosa* population south of Monterey Bay. However, a former Stanford student, Dr. Edward Triplett of the University of California, Santa Barbara, recently sent me *torosa* embryos collected near Santa Barbara, and as they developed it soon became evident that this locality harbors an interesting variant of the southern population. Melanophores were present on the flanks in unusual profusion, and the dorsal bands were weakly represented in comparison with any other *torosa* I have encountered. The almost *rivularis*-like quality of this pattern (Fig. 22) may be an indication that the differentiation of *rivularis* from *torosa* may have had its inception in southern California, before the two stocks began their present northward penetration of the coastal ranges.

These speculations concerning the origins and relationships of the various forms of *Taricha* gain considerable support from comparisons of their blood proteins currently being made in my laboratory by Michael Coates, through the method of "disc electrophoresis." A sample of serum is placed on one end of a cylindrical column of gel which is then subjected to an electric current. The mobility of the various serum proteins, and hence the distances that they move through the gel in response to the current, are determined by the size, shape, and electric charge of their molecules. This results in the accumulation of the proteins at different levels along the length of the column, and when

Taricha granulosa

Taricha torosa torosa (northern California)

Taricha torosa torosa (southern California)

Taricha torosa torosa (near Santa Barbara)

Taricha torosa sierrae (Sierra Nevada)

Taricha rivularis

the column is stained, the proteins show up as a series of sharply defined bands.

In comparing the pattern of bands formed by the sera of the various species and subspecies one can recognize certain protein bands that are common to all *Taricha* and others that may be distinctive of only one or two. The method of electrophoresis thus adds a new and basic criterion for judging genetic relationships between animals, and the goal of Coates' research with *Taricha* is to elucidate events that have taken place at the molecular level during evolution of the genus.

Stated briefly, his results give general support to Riemer's postulate that "the early representatives of the *torosa-sierrae-rivularis* line were most like *torosa*": *granulosa* shares more protein bands with *torosa* than it does with *rivularis*. The greater distinctiveness of the proteins of *rivularis*, as well as of its morphological and behavioral characteristics, is also in keeping with Riemer's belief that this species branched off very early from the *torosa* line. However, the serum comparisons suggest that *torosa* and *sierrae* are neither as closely allied nor separated from one another as recently as Riemer proposes. The protein pattern of *sierrae* does indeed have much in common with that of *torosa*, but it also shares some distinctive bands with that of *rivularis*. The evidence from electrophoresis is also in keeping with the idea of the southern origin of *rivularis*, in that the southern *torosa* proteins resemble the *rivularis* proteins more than do those of northern *torosa*.*

Thus our present inclination is to suggest that all three members of the ancestral *torosa-sierrae-rivularis* line began their differentiation at less disparate times than has been supposed. In any event, we must give credit to the three stocks emerging from a southern California womb for their foresight and discrimination in drifting toward the choicer homes they now occupy in northern California and the Sierra Nevada.

---

* Constance Speaker, working with Dr. Frank Moyer of the Department of Zoology at Washington University, St. Louis, has found additional evidence from electrophoretic studies concerning evolutionary relationships within the genus *Taricha*. Comparisons of certain enzymes in tissues of adult parental and hybrid specimens supplied by us support the conclusions [52, 57] that members of the genus are divisible into two groups, one represented by *granulosa* and the other by *torosa*, *sierrae*, and *rivularis*, and that a *granulosa*-type stock was ancestral to the other three forms.

FIGURE 22. *Young larvae of the species, subspecies, and local variants of* Taricha *thus far encountered in California. Note the small size of* granulosa *compared to other forms. Here, northern California means Santa Cruz County and northward; southern California, Monterey County and southward; Sierra Nevada, its western foothills and slopes. (See map, Fig. 20.)*

NONPROFESSIONAL DIVIDENDS

Whatever its course and cause, I am grateful for this evolutionary flowering that *Taricha* undertook when it crossed the Oregon border and found California so much to its liking. Although my arrival in the West came some few years later, the assortment of species that awaited me was made to order for a scissors-happy microsurgeon, and for the genetic and behavioral studies that eventually followed.

Nor are these scientific benefits the only ones that have accrued from my long association with *Taricha*. I have mentioned earlier the pleasures of the early excursions incidental to discovery of the new species, and I will later elaborate on the unique opportunities for escape and recreation offered by the current program of experiments at my field station in Sonoma County. I should not fail to express my gratitude for another highly enjoyable and less professional privilege that stemmed indirectly from my identification with salamanders.

In late August of 1944 I returned from a vacation in the Sierra Nevada to find a letter awaiting me from a Sacramento physician. Dr. Charles E. von Geldern, having seen a reference to my work, wished to have some information about amphibians he had observed near his fishing cabin on the Klamath River. In replying I apologized for my delay, explaining that I had been in the mountains when his letter arrived, "in search of trout, not salamanders." Almost by return mail came a letter expressing gratification that I shared his passion for these finny creatures, and urging me to utilize at the first opportunity the excellent facilities afforded by his cabin. After a polite interval— about thirty minutes, as I recall—I mailed a reply explaining that by coincidence I was free of teaching duties that particular autumn and was sure I could divest myself of other university responsibilities for a couple of weeks in the near future. Thus began a friendship that made possible a series of vacations at one of the most attractive spots on California's most famous steelhead stream, and for several years my family and I held August free for this sacred purpose. The spawning runs of the steelhead are not in full swing until fall or early winter, but there were usually enough migrants in the river during the summer, especially near the mouths of tributary creeks, to reward the angler who was sufficiently dedicated and industrious. The tributaries themselves were productive of small trout, and so lightly fished that I cannot recall encountering a competitor during the scores of delightful days I waded their canyons. Only rarely did I concern myself—and then only listlessly—with the local salamander fauna. We had our choice of unfrequented river beaches for bathing during the hot afternoons, followed usually by libations with one of the three or four families who constituted our isolated settlement, which was about ten miles upriver from the mining and logging town of Happy Camp. Sunderland, McGinnis, and Fels are treasured names in our memories of the Klamath visits. For making these interludes possible, we shall always be grateful to Dr. von Geldern, one of the most gracious and talented men I have known.

IV

The Peregrinating Pigment Cells

We have already seen how hereditary differences between species (presence or absence of the balancer, contrasting types of mouth armor, slow-versus-rapid rates of growth) lend themselves to the purposes of the analytical embryologist. It is not that he is interested so much in these traits *per se*, but in the opportunities they present to introduce new variables into his experiments and thus to test questions that cannot be explored by use of a single species.

The differences in the larval pigmentation of *torosa* and *rivularis* are a good case in point. To one already addicted by past experience to heteroplastic transplantation of embryonic organs and tissues, the presence of compact bands in *torosa* and their absence in *rivularis* (Fig. 17) was a direct challenge that had to be met by surgical action. The problem is the same as that presented by animals more familiar to the reader: Why, for example, is the zebra striped and the leopard spotted? But these and other mammals are not amenable to experiment in the early developmental stages in which the basis for such differences in color pattern must be sought.

One of the more obvious questions posed by the contrasting patterns was whether the arrangement of the melanophores is controlled by factors intrinsic to these cells themselves, or instead, perhaps, by conditions in the skin tissues in which they develop. The experimental attack was equally obvious: to exchange the young pigment cells between embryos of the two species and see whether they reproduced the arrangements characteristic of their own species or adjusted their pattern to that appropriate to their new setting.

Where They Come From

It might not have been feasible to proceed immediately with this experiment if it had not been for a basic discovery made at about this time by another student of Harrison in the course of his doctoral research at Yale. Almost simultaneously with my first encounter with *rivularis*, Graham DuShane (later, a colleague at Stanford) was beginning to investigate the embryonic origin of amphibian pigment cells. Until then the source of the pigment coloring the skin of vertebrate animals was a strongly debated issue; among other pos- sibilities it was proposed that the pigment-bearing cells arise simply by the *in situ* transformation of ordinary epidermal or connective tissue cells. Harrison's interest in the problem probably came partly from observations made during the course of his early tissue-culture studies, observations disclosing that readily identifiable pigment cells sometimes appeared in his cultures of embryonic spinal cord. Following this clue, DuShane [58] was able to demonstate con- clusively that the chromatophores are indeed of neural origin, arising specifically from an elongate strip of cells lying between the young nerve tube and the overlying epidermis, and designated appropriately as the "neural crest." The crest is formed by the union of the paired neural folds, which meet and fuse in the midline during the closure of the neural tube. DuShane found that surgical removal of the folds resulted in albino larvae (Fig. 23), and also that pieces of fold, when isolated *in vitro* or grafted to the normally unpigmented belly region, delivered chromatophores in profusion. Later it was shown that the pigment cells of other back-boned animals, from lamprey to mammal, stem from this same source, and the neural-crest origin of chromatophores is now one of the well-established and impressive generalizations of comparative vertebrate embryology [59]. (I should add that the pigment cells are by no means the only derivatives of the neural crest, which also gives rise to elements as diverse as the sensory fibers of the spinal and sympathetic nerves, a portion of the adrenal gland, and parts of the skeleton in the head and gill regions.)

This mode of pigment-cell origin is of great practical convenience to the experimenter, since it means that in the early embryonic stages, before the cells' dispersal begins, they are neatly and compactly packaged for surgical manipulation. Later, before they become colored, their migrations carry them to remote and scattered locations in the larva, but in the neural plate or early

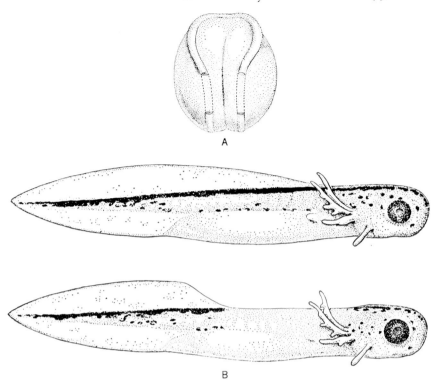

FIGURE 23. *Removal of the neural folds (A) eliminates the source of the skin pigment cells and hence results in albinism (B).*

tail-bud stages they may be excised, grafted, or isolated in aggregates of any desired size. Thus I had reason to be grateful, on deciding to analyze the differences between *torosa* and *rivularis* pigmentation, that DuShane's unpublished discovery of the neural-crest origin of chromatophores had already been made known to me. I have often wondered what our attack would have been if we had not had this information, and how long it might have been—if ever—before we ourselves stumbled upon the source of the cells that had captured our interest.

Figure 24 shows a *torosa* and a *rivularis* larva between which lengths of neural crest were exchanged in the tail-bud stage [60, 61]. Although developing in a foreign skin, the grafted pigment cells have reproduced the patterns proper to their own species. This means the factors responsible for the differences between the *rivularis* and *torosa* patterns, factors that promote banding of the cells in one species and their widespread dispersal in the other, must be sought in the chromatophores themselves, not in the skin. The exchange of

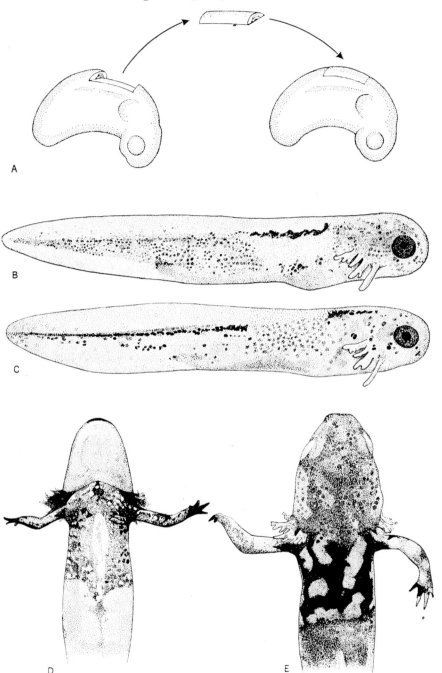

FIGURE 24. *Transplantation of pigment between different species. A: Diagram showing transfer of short length of neural crest from one embryo to*

pigment cells between species thus affords another striking illustration, comparable to those provided by the heteroplastic transplantations decribed earlier, of the overwhelming importance of inborn constitutional factors in shaping developmental behavior.

In relating the results of grafting neural crest between differently pigmented newts to the results of exchanging eyes between rapidly and slowly growing species of *Amblystoma* or gastrula ectoderm between forms with different types of mouth armor, one is reminded that environmental factors are also invariably involved in regulating the expression of hereditary features. And, as we shall see, nowhere is this better illustrated than by the pigment cells [62]. From the time of their origin as part of the neural crest, the fate and behavior of these cells are subject to as wide a gamut of environmental factors as that confronting any other component of the embryo. The ability of given pro-pigment cells actually to achieve pigmentation, the direction and extent of their migration, and the pattern of their ultimate arrangement, are all determined by an array of influences exerted by other tissues of the embryo, as well as by interplay between the developing chromatophores themselves.

How They Become Colored

The young chromatophore is an ameba-like cell that leaves the neural crest and usually completes its excursions before it begins to form pigment in its cytoplasm. The commonest type of pigment cell, the melanophore, derives its name from the dark, granular substance that it synthesizes through enzymatic oxidation of the amino acid tyrosine. Other chromatophores manufacture yellowish and silvery pigments, and are designated xanthophores and guanophores, respectively. The melanophore patterns are the most conspicuous ones in the young newt larva, and we are primarily concerned with these.

The synthesis of melanin within the cells is by no means an automatic or spontaneous process. In manufacturing this pigment, the embryonic melanophore, or melanoblast, leans heavily on neighboring tissues for assistance. A classical example of this dependence was provided by DuShane's experiments with a salamander closely related to *Amblystoma tigrinum*, the "axolotl" of

---

another. B *and* C: rivularis *and* torosa larvae, *respectively, between which neural crest has been exchanged.* D *and* E: Ventral *and dorsal views of a metamorphosing larva of* Taricha *to which neural crest was grafted in the embryonic stage from a donor of the spotted salamander,* Amblystoma punctatum. A, B, C *after Twitty* [60]; D, E *after Twitty and Bodenstein* [61].

Mexico. This animal has been much used for experiments because it can be readily bred in captivity, and it is an especial favorite for pigment studies because albino as well as pigmented stocks are available in several laboratories. DuShane [58] showed that embryos of the albino stock have an abundant supply of potential melanophores, but that these melanoblasts are unable to carry out their pigment-forming functions in the setting afforded by the white axolotl skin. When a square of flank epidermis was removed from a young white axolotl embryo and replaced by epidermis from the "black" strain, the melanoblasts that moved from the white axolotl crest into position beneath the graft differentiated into a conspicuous patch of completely typical melanophores (Fig. 25, A). This pigment-promoting effect of the epidermis is reinforced by the underlying mesoderm.*

How the epidermis and mesoderm exert their effect on the melanoblasts is not yet clear, but whatever the nature of the mechanism, it is a factor that helps regulate the size of the effective melanophore population in all of the salamander species investigated. In *torosa,* for example, whose larvae have a goodly complement of melanophores, the number of these cells would be even greater if it were not for the relatively limited pigment-promoting ability of the environmental tissues. This is evident from the marked increase in the number of melanophores that emerge on the *torosa* flank if a piece of axolotl or *tigrinum* epidermis has been substituted there (Fig. 25, B, C). The supernumerary cells are presumably a portion of the reservoir that normally remains latent or perhaps differentiates at a considerably later larval or even a post-larval stage. It is as if the *torosa* skin is so parsimonious in supplying essential pigment-forming substances to the melanoblasts that competition for the substances becomes a factor in determining the number of these cells that can actually differentiate.

The role of competition was demonstrated by bringing together pigment cells of different stages or rates of development, as, for example, in the experiment illustrated in Figure 26. A single neural fold was removed from an embryo of *torosa* and replaced by one from an embryo of the black axolotl, a species that develops much more rapidly than *torosa.* The two folds later met and fused in the midline, making the neural crest of mixed constitution throughout most of the length of the trunk. As development proceeded, only the grafted axolotl pigment cells gained expression, and both flanks of the host were pigmented exclusively by these cells, which are distinctively different in appearance from *torosa* melanophores. The dominance of the grafted cells clearly derives from the "head start" they have, that is, from their advantage in developmental rate

---

* A former Stanford graduate student, Clark Dalton [64], believes that albinism in the axolotl is partly the result of restraining effects exerted by the skin upon the dispersal of melanoblasts from the neural crest.

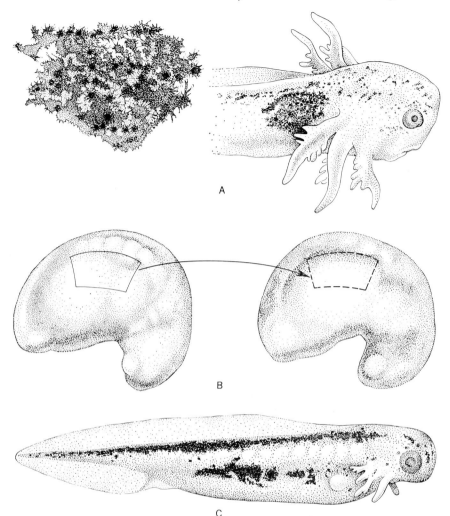

FIGURE 25. *Influence of epidermis on differentiation of skin pigment cells. The albino form of the Mexican salamander, the axolotl, normally has very few pigment cells in its skin, but if a piece of its flank epidermis is replaced by epidermis of a pigmented species, the graft permits the latent host melanophores to differentiate when they move under the graft from the host neural crest (A). Even species that are normally pigmented, like* Taricha torosa, *have a supply of latent, or potential, melanophores that remain unpigmented during larval stages. If a piece of* torosa *epidermis is replaced by epidermis of* Amblystoma tigrinum (B), *the more potent grafted epidermis elicits the differentiation of a greatly increased number of melanophores on the flank (C). (A after Fig. 5, G. P. DuShane, J. Exp. Zool.,* **72**:18.)

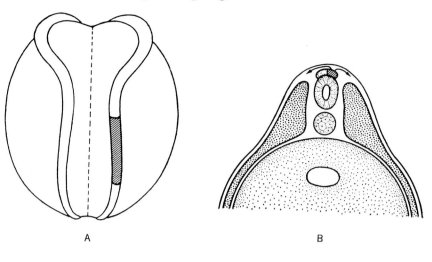

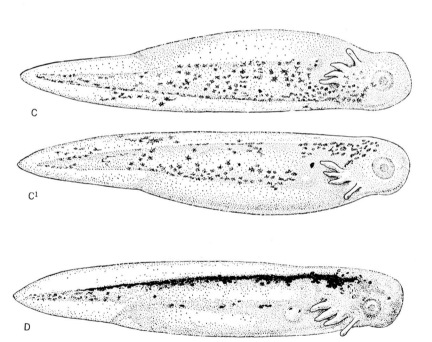

FIGURE 26. *Rapidly differentiating pigment cells suppress the differentiation of slowly developing ones. When one neural fold (source of the pigment cells) of a slowly developing species is replaced by a fold from a rapidly developing one (A), the subsequent fusion of the grafted and host fold during closure of the spinal tube results in a composite neural crest (B). The grafted half of the crest spreads to both sides of the*

and age. Beginning their migrations earlier than the melanoblasts of the host, they "get to the feeding trough first," and by exhausting the ability of the local tissue environment to support pigment synthesis, they forestall development of the tardier host pigment cells [62, 63, 65].

Why They Migrate

One of the fascinating traits of pigment cells is their migratory activity, a feature that sets them apart from the majority of other, more sedentary, cell types in the embryo. As we think of their widespread distribution in the skin, eventually coextensive with the entire body surface in most vertebrate animals, we are not surprised that embryologists were slow to suspect that they are all traceable to such a restricted earlier site as the middorsal line. I have said that the chromatoblasts are ameboid cells, and since an ameboid cell is, almost by definition, a cell capable of active movements, one might say that their dispersal is an automatic consequence of this property. But it is not inevitable that such cells, even though restless, would necessarily make extensive excursions from their point of origin, and, in any event, it is no explanation of the movements merely to say that they "happen." Various proposals have been made concerning the motivation and guidance of their peregrinations. For example, one suggestion is that they may spread beneath the epidermis in response to a chemical attraction exerted by this layer of the skin. Paul Weiss [66] suggests that they may be guided by ultramicroscopic physical pathways present in the skin substratum.

Although I am aware that the environmental tissues may in various ways modify or limit the movements and distribution of chromatophores, I have taken the position that the primary factors responsible for their dissemination are to be sought within the population of pigment cells itself. Just as the character of a roadbed may facilitate or hinder, or at points completely obstruct, the flow of vehicular traffic, so may the character of the epidermal or mesodermal terrain affect the movements of migrating pigment cells, and account in part for regional or species differences in their distribution. But my experience with these cells indicates that the actual incentive behind their movements is supplied primarily, not by factors in the tissue environment, but by influences exerted

---

host, and inhibits the differentiation of the host pigment cells that disperse later. Both flanks of the host become pigmented exclusively by the highly distinctive chromatophores of the donor species (C and C¹), as may be seen by comparison with D, a normal larva of the host species. From Twitty [62].

upon one another by the developing chromatophores themselves through excitatory chemical substances that they release.

To begin with, the results of simple transplantation experiments [62, 67] such as those represented in Figure 27 seem to discount the importance of environmental pulls or pathways in the guidance of cell migration from the neural crest. In normal development, as indicated in Figure 27, A, the pigment cells originate dorsally and descend along the dorso-ventral axis. If, however, as in Figure 27, B, the crest is removed from its normal dorsal location, and shifted to a position well down on the side, then we find that the chromatophores migrate quite as readily against the dorso-ventral axis as they do with it. The cells spread first dorsally from the graft and then continue across the middorsal line in numbers sufficient to colonize the opposite flank. The embryo appears to offer a trackless terrain to the pigment cells; wherever they are set down, they are inclined to spread radially in all directions. They will not, however, invade territory already occupied by cells of their own kind (Fig. 28).

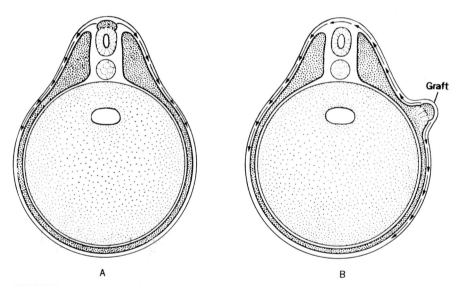

A   B

FIGURE 27. *In normal development the pigment cells spread ventrally from the neural crest (A). But they also move dorsally, as seen when the crest is displaced to a position well down on the side of the embryo (B). In moving first dorsally and then ventrally, to colonize the opposite flank, the grafted pigment cells show that the movements of chromatophores are independent of any directional pulls or pathways that might be postulated to explain their dispersion in normal development. From Twitty [62].*

The best evidence that such mutual interplay is an important factor in pigment-cell dispersal came from experiments in which neural crest was cultured *in vitro*. The embryonic chromatophores readily took to life outside the embryo. When a piece of neural crest was placed in a drop of saline or body fluid, it attached itself firmly to the glass substratum and within two or three days pro-pigment cells began to creep out from the main mass and scatter radially (Fig. 29). We then modified the conditions in the drop, so that one portion of the outgrowth spread as usual on the glass surface, openly exposed to the full volume of medium, while the remainder advanced beneath a small fragment of coverslip held slightly aloft by vaseline under its two ends (Fig. 30, A). Under these conditions it is safe to assume that the portion of the culture invading the low-ceilinged chamber will almost immediately become subjected to a higher concentration of any diffusible substances released by the cells than can possibly accumulate in the much larger volume of medium to which the remainder of the culture is directly exposed [68].

The results of this experiment were consistent and usually quite striking (Fig. 30, B, C). Upon entering the space beneath the glass fragment, cells began to migrate more actively and became more widely separated than those spreading elsewhere on the substratum. Those which escaped their confinement by spreading beyond the opposite edge of the fragment immediately lost impetus and again assumed a more crowded arrangement. Time-lapse motion pictures were especially useful in recording and analyzing these phenomena.

If it is indeed true that chromatoblasts are motivated to move by influences exerted by their neighbors, then it should follow that single isolated cells will be deprived of migratory impetus and remain stationary. By the same token, cells isolated in intimate groups of two or more should exhibit mutual antagonism and move away from one another in directed response to graded concentrations of their diffusible products. To test these assumptions, Dr. Niu and I isolated cells in capillary tubes of very small bore, since a narrow, axiate enclosure is by design best suited for the establishment of well-organized diffusion gradients [39, 69]. Fluid from the body cavity of adult *Taricha* was used as culture medium instead of saline, since cells isolated singly or in small numbers are especially sensitive to their environment and are more likely to thrive in a medium whose composition has already been conditioned by association with other cells.

The technique for isolating the cells is illustrated in Figure 31. Neural crest was explanted in drops of body fluid, and after chromatoblasts had begun to move out upon the glass substratum they were detached by gentle manipulation with the tip of a pipette and drawn into its capillary portion by oral suction

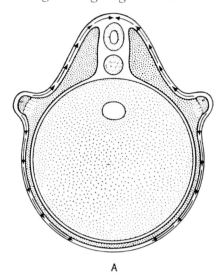

A

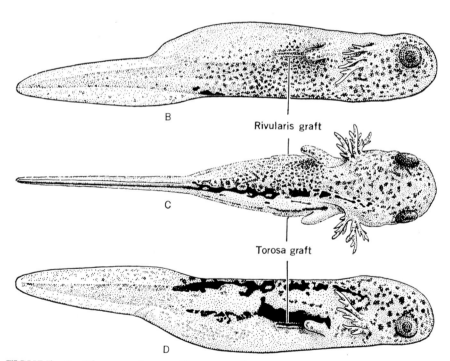

B

Rivularis graft

C

Torosa graft

D

FIGURE 28. *Chromatophores will not invade territory already occupied by other migrating pigment cells. This is seen when neural crest is grafted to both sides of an embryo whose own crest has been removed (A). The movements of both groups of pigment cells are halted when they meet*

applied through a rubber tube. The capillary portion was then broken off and placed in a shallow dish, where it was secured by pushing one end into a mass of vaseline.

The behavior of a large number of cells, each isolated singly, was followed carefully, and the observations were remarkably consistent. In no capillary tube was a cell observed to execute migratory excursions over a distance greater than a few (possibly three or four) cell diameters, and in the majority of the tubes the movements were even more limited than this. The cells underwent active, almost constant, changes in shape, indistinguishable from those of cells belonging to large colonies, but their movements patently lacked sustained directional impetus. This was particularly evident in motion-picture records, which showed short advances promptly cancelled by reversal of direction, as the cell shuffled repeatedly back and forth within the same limited span. In observing these films one could not resist the impression that the cells were highly charged with migratory potential and in need of only the slightest external differential or "push" to send them along.

The migratory behavior of cells isolated in pairs or groups of three or four usually contrasted sharply with that typical of single cells. Instead of remaining essentially stationary, as cells without close neighbors did, they characteristically moved well apart from one another. This response was not invariable, nor of uniform magnitude, but the average excursion was so very much greater than that of solitary cells that there could be no question whatever that mutual influences were operating. Figure 32 presents a typical comparison of the results with one, two, and three cells, respectively. In general, the average excursion per cell was roughly proportional to the number of cells present, and when larger groups were isolated the total distance traveled by individual cells was often relatively enormous.*

* The force of the migratory impetus is dramatically illustrated when migrating pigment cells encounter an obstacle, such as a glass-wool fiber lying on the coverslip at right angles to the direction of their movement, and persist in squeezing beneath it. Ordinarily only the more compressible parts of the cell can wedge beneath the glass-wool fiber, leaving an entrapped portion containing the rigid yolk platelets abundant in young embryonic cells. This may result in extreme attenuation of the advancing migratory tip of the cell, sometimes leading to tensions strong enough to rupture the entrapped portion of the cell. Figure 33 shows the stretching and orientation of the cells of a culture encountering a glass-wool fiber, and the attenuated tip of a single cell at high magnification.

in the middorsal line, as is evident when the two grafts come from species whose pigment cells are readily distinguished from one another. This is clear from B, C, and D, showing right and left sides and also the dorsal view of a host bearing a rivularis *graft on one side and a* torosa *graft on the other. A from Twitty [62]; B, C, and D from Twitty [67].*

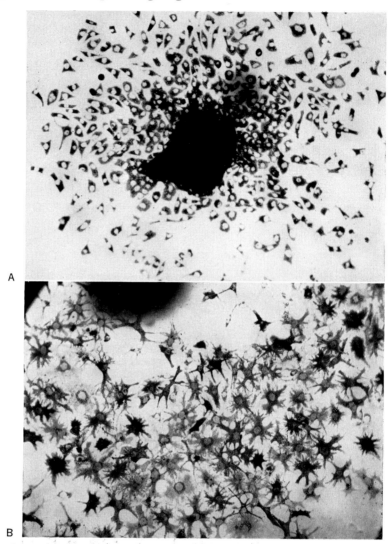

FIGURE 29. A: *Young outgrowth of* T. rivularis *pigment cells, after they have dispersed widely from the neural-crest explant, but before they have begun to synthesize pigment and become highly branched.* B: *Portion of an older outgrowth of* T. rivularis *crest, after the pigment cells have become fully differentiated.*

Our working hypothesis is that cellular products are active in chromatoblast migration. There is little, if any concrete information about the chemical identity of such cellular products. Simple acidity gradients, resulting from production and diffusion of respiratory carbon dioxide, might be responsible. Reed

Flickinger, one of my graduate students, adopted this view tentatively and provided some evidence in its behalf. The construction of experiments to test decisively the possible role of such gradients is actually more difficult technically than one might assume.

Of the several other questions raised by our observations of cells isolated singly, in pairs, and in small groups I shall mention only one, namely, whether mutual stimulation operates only in the dispersal of neural-crest cells, or is a concept that is widely applicable to other migratory cell types as well. This is a question of more than academic interest, since the migratory habit of malignant cells leads to their invasion of other tissues and to their entry into the blood stream. Our tests of other cell types have been limited to those of subcutaneous mouse tumors, and of normal connective-tissue of the embryonic-chick heart. The cells were allowed to spread into the confined spaces beneath low-hanging fragments of coverslip. As in the identical experiments with neural-crest extracts, the cells responded with increased migration rates and wider intercellular spacing [62]. When cell types as diverse in origin as these three display such similar manifestations, there is considerable reason for concluding that mutual activation is indeed widespread in its operation among migratory tissues. Whether the chemical mediation is the same or different for each cell type, or complex or simple in nature, are questions that remain without answers. At this point I can record some surprise that we ever came to ask such questions, considering that the whole investigation had its remote origin in the chance discovery of a new species of newt on a June outing in the Mendocino County mountains.

Why They Form Stripes

In concluding this section of the book we may return to the feature that first provoked our attack on chromatophore development, namely the eye-catching differences in pigment pattern distinguishing the larvae of *torosa* and *rivularis*. The pattern of *rivularis* is readily interpreted in terms of the thesis that we have just been developing, namely, that mutual activation causes the chromatoblasts to become widely and uniformly dispersed. But can this view be harmonized with the banded pattern of *torosa,* in which the concentration of virtually all the melanophores into a pair of compact dorsal stripes would seem to be in direct conflict with any explanation of pigment-cell movements based on the principle of "negative attraction"?

This apparent contradiction has been resolved by showing that the grouping of the *torosa* melanophores into bands is the consequence of a secondary reag-

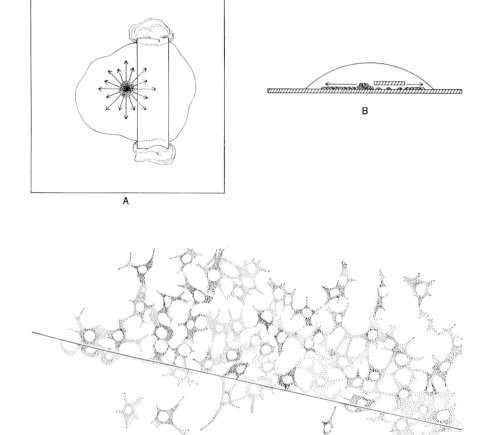

FIGURE 30. *Acceleration of pigment-cell migration when developing under conditions conducive to accumulation of stimulating substances produced by the cells. A: The explant of neural crest is placed at one side of a fragment of coverslip held slightly aloft from the primary coverslip by an intervening film of vaseline at each end. Solid and broken arrows rep-*

gregation that follows a primary phase in which they are distributed uniformly and more widely on the flanks. Dispersal and reaggregation can be observed in the embryo under both normal and experimental conditions, and to even better advantage after isolation of crest *in vitro* [67]. Figure 34 shows the sequence of events in a culture of *torosa* melanophores developing in a drop of coelomic fluid. During the first few days, the cells emigrated freely from the explant and assumed a widespread distribution. With the onset of pigment formation, however, they began to draw together into closer association, eventually forming compact clusters in which the individual cells were for the most part quite indistinguishable. The mass of melanophores ringing the explant in Figure 34, F may be likened to the bands that form through cellular reaggregation in the young larva.

Since the phenomenon of reaggregation involves cell movement, one is perhaps inclined to visualize it in terms of active migration of the melanophores. It is believed, however, that the mechanism is quite unrelated to that by which these cells achieve their original dispersal. As migratory activity begins to decline following emigration from the explant, the cytoplasmic processes of the differentiating melanophores become increasingly elongate and ramifying, and characteristically develop firm adhesions with the processes of neighboring cells; as a consequence, the culture becomes an intricate supracellular meshwork. With the onset of reaggregation, however, the interconnecting processes appear to undergo a shortening or retraction, and our observations suggest that the resultant tensions are at least partly responsible for drawing the cells into increasingly close proximity.

Whatever its mechanism, reaggregation is possible only under conditions conducive to full and normal differentiation of the melanophores. This conclusion is based on comparison of the behavior just described with that of cultures developing in physiological salt solution, which is suitable for the migration and prolonged maintenance of chromatophores *in vitro* but permits only limited pigmentary differentiation. Outgrowths in this medium scatter freely, but they become incompletely pigmented, and they show little if any evidence

resent, respectively, the portions of the pigment-cell culture spreading on the uncovered and covered portions of the primary coverslip. B: Schematic representation (in cross section of the drop of culture medium) showing the scattered distribution of the pigment cells while passing beneath the fragment, and the crowded arrangement which they assume after escaping beyond its opposite margin. C: Drawing of actual culture, showing widely spaced cells beneath the fragment of coverslip, and cells that have crowded together again after emerging from the opposite margin of the fragment. After Twitty and Niu [68].

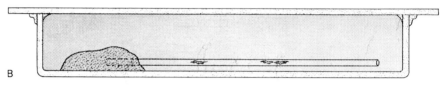

FIGURE 31. *Method used for isolating pigment cells singly or in small clusters in fine-bore capillary tubes. A: When the cells begin to emigrate from the piece of neural crest they are sucked into the capillary tip of a pipette, which is then broken off and stored in a dish of saline (B). The capillary tip is held in position by imbedding one end in a mound of vaseline. After Twitty and Niu [39].*

of the subsequent reaggregation that is characteristic of cultures developing in coelomic fluid.

Granting, however, that the pigment bands form by aggregation of cells originally widely dispersed, the question remains why the melanophores choose the dorsal margins of the trunk muscle masses (myotomes) as the site for their alignment. There appears to be no *a priori* reason why the cells should not, for example, instead of retracting dorsally, draw together ventrally to form bands lower on the sides. The clue to this phenomenon lies in a fact not mentioned previously: that conditions for pigment formation in developing melanophores become decreasingly favorable along the dorso-ventral axis of the embryo. For example, pigment appears earlier and darkens more rapidly when neural crest is grafted to situations high on the flank than when it is implanted lower on the side [71]. Applying this finding to the problem at hand, one reasons that melanophores scattered over the flanks do not all differentiate at a uniform rate. Those situated dorsally will mature more rapidly, and, by the same token,

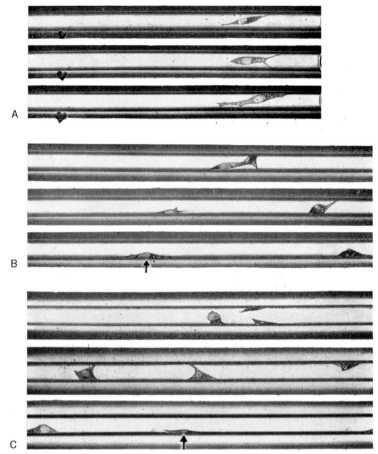

FIGURE 32. *Cells isolated singly (A) in capillary tubes remain essentially station-ary, while those isolated in pairs or larger groups (B and C) move away from one another in response to diffusible substances released by the cells. From Twitty and Niu [39].*

will be the first to fulfill the conditions necessary for reaggregation, since this ensues only with advancing differentiation. Keeping in mind the mechanism by which reaggregation is apparently accomplished, namely, retraction of inter-connecting processes, one almost inevitably reaches the conclusion that outlying cells would gradually be drawn dorsally, toward the region where these ten-sions first develop. The sequence of events is illustrated in Figure 35, which represents the original dispersed arrangement of the melanoblasts and their sub-sequent withdrawal into a band capping the dorsal margin of the trunk muscu-

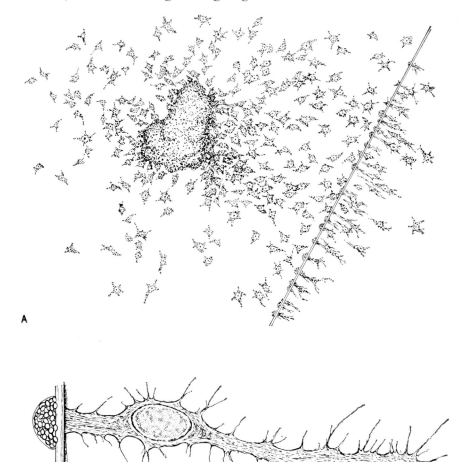

FIGURE 33. *Pigment cells squeezing beneath an impediment placed in their pathway. A: Drawing of culture showing many cells entrapped by glasswool fiber. B: Single cell showing great attenuation of advancing tip. See footnote, p. 89. (After Figs. 15 and 16, F. T. Algard, J. Exp. Zool., 123:518–9.)*

lature. There is also a concentration of melanophores on the spinal cord, and this median aggregation is linked at intervals to the paired bands by interconnecting melanophores.

If it is true that these dorsalmost tissues, the spinal cord and myotome margins, are indeed points toward which differentiating melanophores are prone to aggregate, then it should be possible to shift the site of band formation by corresponding displacements of these tissues themselves. This was done by the procedures illustrated in Figure 36, with the object of displacing the spinal cord and dorsal myotome margins to a more ventral position on the flank while leaving the neural crest in its normal dorsal position. In order that the displaced

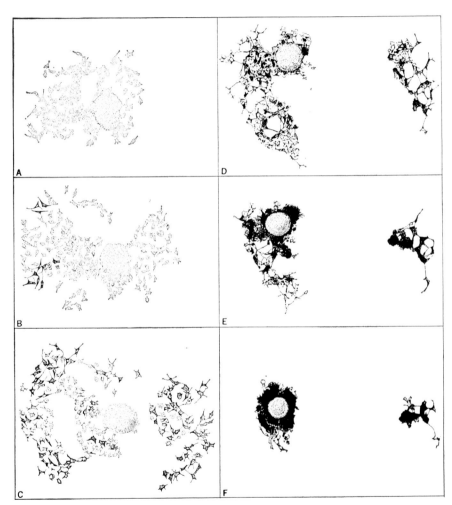

FIGURE 34. *Duplication* in vitro *of the reaggregation of melanophores shown in Figure 35. The embryonic pigment cells first spread out widely from the explant of neural crest (A and B), but as they begin to differentiate (C) they draw into increasingly close association (D and E) until eventually most of them are grouped closely again around the explant from which they originally dispersed (F). From Twitty [67].*

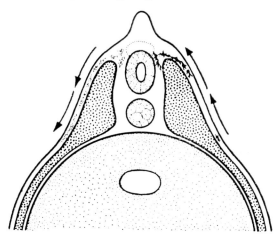

FIGURE 35. *Schematic drawing illustrating the sequence of events leading to dorsal band formation in* T. torosa. *At first (left) the melanophores become distributed uniformly over the entire lateral faces of the developing axial musculature (myotomes), but subsequently (right) all of them, except for an occasional outlying one, draw together dorsally to become densely aggregated along the dorsal margins of the myotomes and upon the spinal cord. From Twitty* [62].

nerve tube would not itself be a source of melanophores, a crest-free cord was produced by removing the neural folds from a *torosa* embryo. After closure of the neural plate, the crestless tube and the adjacent somites of one side were removed as a single block, and implanted upside down in substitution of the somites of another embryo of the same age. Since the neural crest of the host was not disturbed, it remained as a source—and the only source—of the melanophores that would subsequently supply the graft. The results in a typical case are shown in Figure 36. Of the total complement of melanophores issuing from the host crest at the level of the inverted graft, a majority confirmed my expectation by aggregating into a ventrally placed band.

As we saw earlier, the secondary rearrangements leading to band formation also take place when *torosa* melanophores are developing on a *rivularis* host. Since this shows that the same environmental factors are operating in *rivularis* as in *torosa*, we must now ask why the *rivularis* melanophores are unresponsive to them and remain permanently dispersed. The answer seems to lie, at least in part, in genetically controlled differences in the level of differentiation attained by the melanophores of the two species. Even *torosa* melanophores, we may recall, do not reaggregate except under conditions that are conducive to an active tempo and eventually to a high peak of pigmentary development. When these conditions are not fulfilled, as in the case of cultures developing in physiological salt solution, the melanophores remain permanently scattered. The suggestion is offered that the stable arrangement of *rivularis* melanophores is associated with their inherently lower rate of development and final level of differentiation compared with that of *torosa* pigment cells. Both in normal development and when growing *in vitro,* the melanophores of *rivularis* require a longer period for the onset of melanization, and at their peak of differentiation are less heavily pigmented, than those of *torosa.* If reaggregation of the pigment cells in *torosa* is indeed a threshold phenomenon, depending upon the realization of a given level of chromatophore differentiation, then one is perhaps justified in correlating the absence of reaggregation in *rivularis* with the failure of its melanophores to achieve the peak of development requisite for setting this phenomenon into play.

LIKE CELLS, LIKE ANIMALS

H. E. Lehman, who did graduate work at Stanford, has made major contributions to the further understanding of salamander pigment patterns, including the factors determining the differentiation and distribution of the other two categories of chromatophores. In *torosa,* for example, although the melanophores are the most conspicuous component of the color pattern, closer inspection of older larvae reveals the presence of a deep-lying layer of silvery pigment cells (guanophores) on the lower flank and belly. Ingenious experiments showed that the emergence of the guanophores in this position is controlled by the overlying area of the skin, which with advancing age becomes selectively conducive to the differentiation of this type of chromatophore [72]. Altogether, Lehman's work provides some of the strongest confirmatory evidence available concerning the decisive roles of the environmental tissues in regulating pigment synthesis and chromatophore patterns.

The yellow pigment cells, xanthophores, play a prominent part in the pigment pattern of young axolotl larvae, in which clusters of them alternate with melanophore aggregates to form a barred pattern along the trunk. Lehman has shown that the emigration of melanophores from the neural crest precedes slightly that of the xanthophores, and proposes that this difference, together with selective cellular affinities within the chromatoblast population, is responsible for the axolotl pigment pattern.

In commenting on the multiplicity of factors regulating the contributions of melanophores, guanophores, and xanthophores to the totality of vertebrate pigmentation, Lehman and Youngs [73] liken the problems to "those encountered in the ecological analysis of species distribution. The concepts of limiting fac-

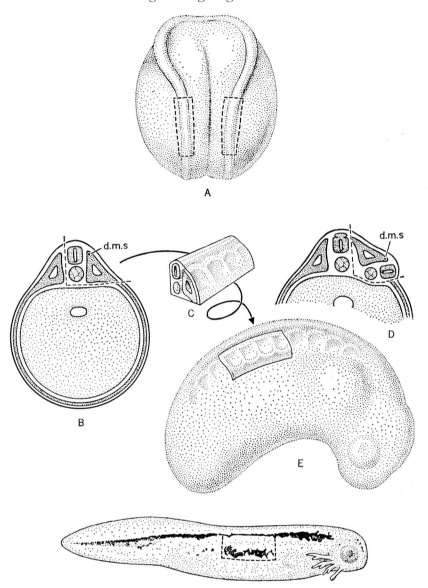

FIGURE 36. *Experiment showing that the spinal cord and dorsal margin of the muscle masses are the preferred site for band formation in* T. torosa *even when these structures have been inverted so that they lie on the side of the embryo. After extirpation of the trunk folds (A) and the subsequent closure of the "crestless" nerve tube (B), the block of tissue*

tors, territorialism, population pressure, and niche, long used by ecologists to explain the localization and spread of species, are in many ways analogous to conditions within the embryo that regulate the fate and distribution of differentiating pigment cells."

It is perhaps this similarity in the populations at the two levels, cellular and organismic, that made it so easy for me to transfer my attentions from the peregrinations of embryonic chromatophores—inside and outside the embryo, but always in the laboratory—to the excursions of whole adult newts to and from their breeding streams in the mountains of Sonoma County. There were indeed other motivations for this shift of interest, and these will be exposed in the following section of the book. Whatever the causes, and whether for better or for worse, the fact is that for the past several years wading boots and the four-wheel-drive Jeep have figured more prominently in my research than iris shears and dissecting scope.

---

represented in C was cut out and grafted upside down in substitution of the muscle segments of another embryo (D and E). This translocation of the spinal cord and dorsal margins of the myotomes (d.m.s.) results in a corresponding displacement in the site of band formation by the melanophores issuing from the intact neural crest of the host (F). From Twitty [67].

V

The Pepperwood Creek Affair

The reader may already have sensed that my devotion to newts is not entirely unrelated to the charms of the places where they live and love. If there is a friendlier and more pleasant setting than the small brook of the California coastal mountains, I have yet to find it. Some of my friends have been unkind enough to suggest that my affection for this environment stems more from the trout it harbors than from the opportunity it affords for the detached study of newt reproduction and behavior. The dedicated biologist, especially the one who has deserted the laboratory for less-hallowed surroundings, must steel himself against such charges and go his lonely way, remote from the council chambers where his colleagues enjoy the solid satisfactions of committee assignments. Where the newts beckon, their follower must go, and if this exposes him to the harshness of the California springtime, and to the company of associates and students who share his distaste for the barbecue pit and other Spartan features of a well-equipped field station—well, this is the price he must pay with all the fortitude he can muster.

To come more directly to the point, what turned out to be a full-scale project began as a quite tentative and unpretentious undertaking. One cannot become as deeply involved as I had in the systematics of a genus of organisms without wondering about such things as the nature and extent of the evolutionary divergence that the species have undergone. For example, have the species of *Taricha,* during their descent from a *granulosa*-like forebear, reached the point where their intactness as separate species is now safe against the inroads of possible interbreeding? There are various protections against exchange of genes between species, including lack of contact, as when they occupy different geographic ranges or ecological niches. However, this type of isolation may disappear with changing distributions or habitat tolerances, and the evolutionary separation of two or more species does not become truly irrevocable until more deep-seated barriers to interbreeding develop. These include behavioral or even anatomical differences that block interspecific mating, and especially, fundamental genetic incompatibilities such as inviability or infertility of any hybrids that might be formed.

Shortly after discovery of the new forms we found that the species of *Taricha* could be readily hybridized in all interspecific combinations. Eggs removed from the oviducts of spawning females and treated with sperm suspensions prepared from males of other species developed normally through the subsequent embryonic and larval periods. But if crossbreeding is to have any evolutionary potentialities or consequences, it is not enough that the hybrids be viable; they must also be fertile and hence able to produce further generations of offspring. Although we made earnest efforts to rear the hybrids for tests of their fertility, we had little success in growing them to maturity. There was no reason to attribute this to genetic causes, since we encountered the same difficulties in attempts to rear the parental species. The principal problem lay in inducing the juveniles to feed following metamorphosis and emergence from the water. In seeking a solution, I decided that we should entrust the problem to Mother Nature, by releasing artificially produced hybrids and hoping that they would find a more tempting bill-of-fare outdoors than we had been able to supply them in the laboratory.*

In the meantime, however, I had become absorbed with embryological experiments on *Taricha,* and for several years the idea of a hybrid-planting program was at best an idle one. It very probably would have remained latent except for a casual trip with a fisherman friend, Robert McGrouther, to a Sonoma County ranch owned by one of his business acquaintances.

The Newt Ranch

The word "ranch" did not—and does not—adequately describe this piece of real estate, especially to a middle westerner like myself who is still inclined to

---

* Later we learned how to rear *Taricha* to maturity in the laboratory, but I am glad that this success did not come until after the Pepperwood Creek Affair was already well under way.

envision the typical rural holding as a quarter section of flat cornland. When I found instead a fourteen-thousand acre mountainous expanse of virgin forest and springtime meadows drained by *rivularis*-ridden streams, I recognized instantly that further postponement of a hybrid-planting program would be inexcusable indeed. Actually, about a year passed before I revealed my aspirations to the owner, Mr. Roy Hedgpeth, in a letter that placed due stress on the importance of the project and the unique suitability of his ranch as a site for its conduct. If the proposal met with his approval I would bring a few students to the ranch three or four times each spring to make artificial cross-fertilizations of eggs for release in a suitable stream. Since weather was often uncertain at that season, we might need to pitch a tent or erect an inconspicuous lean-to as shelter for our sleeping bags. This was truly all I had in mind. But Mr. Hedgpeth's response exceeded my hopes and expectations. In effect, he conceded that the project seemed to have merit, but felt that my conception of the facilities it would require reflected negative thinking. It so happened, he explained, that a certain house on the ranch had been little used in recent years except to accommodate occasional guests, and if I chose to occupy it as headquarters he would gladly recondition it and present me with the keys for as long as might be required. The ranch is remotely situated, and there were no facilities for immediate reply by wire or phone, but in a letter that tried not to seem over-eager, I made it clear that his terms were quite acceptable.

Thus the Pepperwood Creek Affair was born. My first inspection of the house was made in February 1953, in the company of McGrouther, and I sensed instantly that, henceforth, experimental embryology was destined to give way increasingly to natural history. A few dishpans had to be put into emergency use until a leaky roof could be repaired and eventually replaced, and some time passed before we completed installation of all the necessary household and laboratory appurtenances; but the house (Fig. 37) was comfortable and spacious, its setting scenic, and its location convenient, close by a stream ideally suited for our purposes. Not often is an impecunious professor granted long-term tenancy and almost-unrestricted use of a protected mountain domain that most university presidents—and maybe even trustees—would covet. Opportunities like this make one recognize the extent of one's debt to one's science! A professor of physics or engineering might well feel pangs of guilt for making frequent visits to pastoral retreats, but as a biologist committed to the study of newts, I make the 150-mile drive from Stanford to El Rancho Seto Sendero in the serene and righteous knowledge that I am responding to the relentless demands of scholarship.

After many scores of these trips, arrival at the ranch still brings the same feelings of elation, discovery, and renewal that I experienced on the first visit. After

FIGURE 37. *House serving as laboratory and living quarters for the Pepperwood Creek Affair. The sign in the foreground reads: "Stanford University —Dr. V. Twitty—Do not disturb wildlife on this or adjoining parts of the Hedgpeth Ranch." The wording is by the original owner of the ranch, who installed similar signs throughout the study area, thus assuring me of considerable stature in the eyes of visitors. One friend, given to vivid and even profane language, expostulated on arrival: "——— ———, Vic, I thought maybe you'd bought the ——— ——— ranch." The platform attached at the right of the house was added by Mr. Hedgpeth to support large redwood tanks, fed by gravity from a nearby spring, for the storage and study of newts. Not visible (at the rear of the house) is an outdoor living area where on balmy evenings the rekindled barbecue fire inspires many fruitful— or at least spirited—scientific discussions.*

all, one enters a different world there. Usually our only neighbors are the families of the ranch foremen, Fred and Peter Radtkey, two and a half miles away. The ranch supports four or five thousand sheep, but they are scattered over fourteen thousand acres, and at times they almost seem outnumbered by deer and other game. A vivid recollection from our first spring at the ranch somehow typifies its atmosphere. As we climbed out of a stream where we had been looking for newts, we met two of the ranch hands bearing behind their saddles two incidental by-products of their mission to a distant part of the ranch. One was a prominently tusked wild hog and the other a steelhead trout of impressive size. The well-dressed rancher seldom ventures forth without his side arm, and these resourceful gentlemen had collected the hog for its tasty flesh, and undoubtedly had defended themselves against attack by the savage steelhead while fording a creek. Sights like this, not unusual in northwestern Sonoma County, are almost never encountered in Palo Alto or on the Stanford Campus!

The peak of our activity at the ranch is during the newt breeding season in the spring, but in recent years we have ingeniously devised extensions of the project that often require—or at least help justify—our presence there at other seasons of the year. Early summer is especially delightful, and even the hot spells that sometimes strike later are no longer unwelcome, now that we have learned to cool ourselves each afternoon in a secluded canyon pool only a few hundred yards from the house. The work itself, although often physically demanding and even exhausting, is hardly of the type that is conducive to hypertension. It does not leave the imagination unstimulated, however, judging from the inspired discussions that invariably seem to develop evenings around the wood stove or rekindled barbecue fire. Time and again we have arrived at brilliant and esoteric solutions to the difficult problems of homing behavior and speciation in newts, only to realize at breakfast the next morning that our insight had somehow clouded overnight. Even tape recordings have failed to capture and preserve the splendor of our ideas; for some reason the playbacks always fall grievously short of our expectations.

We have wished at times that the ranch were located closer to our home base at Stanford, and especially that the final thirty miles of narrow and winding mountain road could somehow be straightened and widened. A few additional feet of passing space would have saved us from being forced off the road into a stream bed forty feet below, on a stormy day several years ago when our Jeep station wagon was heavily loaded with a season's supply of staple foods. No serious injuries were sustained, although we had a bad moment or two before recognizing that the gory material on Dr. Niu's forehead was strawberry jam. But a few hazards and inconveniences are a small price to pay for the privilege of the seclusion we enjoy at the ranch.

Mired Even Deeper

I think it will be clear from the preceding section that the hybrid-planting program was undertaken with more enthusiasm than planning and foresight.

We did have a solid purpose in mind, namely, to let nature perform a chore—the rearing of hybrids to maturity—that we had found difficult in the laboratory. We were vaguely aware of other possible dividends of the project, but almost our sole concern during the first spring at the ranch was to cross-fertilize as many eggs as possible for subsequent release in a selected stream. Accordingly, we—my graduate students and I—set up an assembly-line operation that would grind out the maximum number of hybrids in the limited time available. Eggs were dissected from the oviducts of spawning *rivularis* females, dipped briefly in a saline suspension of sperm taken from *torosa* males, and set aside in shallow baking dishes (we bought them by the gross) to develop to the hatching stage [74]. During the several visits to the ranch that first spring we made a total of about twenty thousand infant hybrids in this way—eventually we were to achieve outputs of half this number in a single day. (As in many cooperative efforts competition often reared its head, and I remember days when each of us sat for hours in grim determination to fill more baking dishes than any of his collaborators. I was reminded of my own graduate-school days when we had vied to see who could graft more limb buds or eye vesicles during a single session at the dissecting microscope.)

Even before we released our first season's hybrids, with benedictions and blessings for their survival, an alarming possibility occurred to us. Even if our assumption that some of them would escape predators and other hazards and grow to maturity was correct, what assurance could we have that they would not scatter over the whole countryside and eventually select different streams for breeding—maybe even streams in the next county, where we could not hope to find them?

By considering this possibility, we were immediately faced with the question: Do newts have a fixed home range to which they confine themselves throughout their lives, or are their yearly movements to and from the water of a random nature, perhaps carrying them to new breeding sites each year? I was familiar, as any biologist and most laymen would be, with a few classical examples of animal loyalty to a place of birth, such as the return of spawning salmon from the ocean to their home stream, and the prodigiously long flights that certain species of birds make to visit the same nesting sites each year. A quick look at some of the amphibian literature revealed examples of the affinity some frogs and toads have for their accustomed breeding ponds. But there seemed to be little information about home range and homing behavior in salamanders, and none at all pertaining to home-loving qualities of western newts.

Almost before we knew it, then, we had mired even deeper into field biology, and were forced to become students not only of newt speciation, but also of newt behavior. In fact, this latter aspect of the Pepperwood Creek Affair has occupied an increasing proportion of our time and efforts, and I shall take the liberty of describing our studies on homing before returning to the account of our hybridization experiments.

California newts take about four to six years to reach maturity, and naturally we were reluctant to wait this long to see whether the first batch of hybrids would return to the places where we had released them as newly hatched larvae. Accordingly we chose to put our questions to the native *rivularis* population instead, on the assumption—since confirmed—that their behavior would be the same as that of the hybrids. Using breeding adults, mostly males, we began giving them identifying marks that would permit subsequent recognition and hence tell us whether they returned in later years to the same segments of the stream in which they had originally been found and marked. From this beginning our tests branched out. Instead of releasing the marked adults in the same part of the stream from which they were collected, we displaced them to other portions of the same stream, or to increasingly remote locations in other streams. Special enclosures were built to test their ability to orient (detect directions) after displacement. Surgical interference with sight and olfaction was used to study the importance of these senses in guiding migration. These and other experiments on homing, as well as information about other aspects of newt biology accruing as a by-product of this study, will be discussed further. But first it is necessary to set the background for the experiments by describing the seasonal habits of *rivularis* and picturing for the reader the setting in which our studies have been conducted.

Pepperwood Creek and Its Newts

The aerial photograph (Fig. 38) provides an eagle's eye view of the entire study area and the streams within which and between which newts have been displaced for studies of their homing behavior. The hub of our operations is the portion of Pepperwood Creek* indicated by a broken line and dubbed for convenience "the experimental stretch." For recording the locations of captures and recaptures of marked animals, this stretch has been divided into a series of 58 segments or "stations," each approximately fifty yards long and identified by a large numeral painted on a tree or boulder near the streamside. Along the winding course of the stream channel, the length of the experimental stretch

---

* So named because of the handsome tree, also known as California laurel, myrtlewood, or bay tree, that is abundant along its course. I had known it near Stanford by the last of these names, and during my first season at the ranch I pointed to a huge specimen and asked the 12-year-old son of the foreman if it was not a bay tree. "Yes," was the deadpan reply, "but we call it Pepperwood for short."

FIGURE 38. *Aerial photograph of study area (bottom is north).*

is about one and one-half miles, but the direct air-line distance is very slightly more than one mile. Its upstream end is marked by the confluence of Grasshopper Creek, and a few hundred yards downstream from there the stretch receives its only live tributary, Churchman Creek. The downstream end of the stretch is marked by the point where Pepperwood Creek enters a meadow. Beyond this point the stream usually disappears by midsummer into the gravelly meadow floor, emerging several hundred yards downstream where the channel enters a wooded canyon.

This stretch of stream was chosen because of its accessibility (a ranch road parallels its course), its small size and hence easy "wadeability," and perhaps, above all, because of the abundance of newts that use it for breeding. To give some idea of the size of its *rivularis* population, I might mention that between 1953 and 1959 we removed over 24,000 females from the experimental stretch, partly for use in the hybridization experiments. That is a lot of water dogs. The heavy withdrawal took its toll, of course, but the breeding population is still amply large for our purposes. At times, in fact, after strenuous days of wading its length to record marked animals, we wish we had been even more ruthless in reducing the number of its residents.

The newts that breed in the experimental stretch descend in the spring from the adjoining mountains, particularly from the steep and heavily wooded slope to the south. During the dry summer months they hide in underground retreats where they can find moisture; with the first heavy autumn rains they begin to emerge and forage for food on the forest floor [75, 76]. They are strictly carnivorous [77], and we have observed stubborn tugs-of-war as two newts compete for a favorite morsel such as an earthworm. Surface foraging is confined to periods of high humidity, during late afternoon or night or when rain is falling. The bioclimatology of the breeding migration of *rivularis* was the subject of a doctoral research project by Wayne Packer [75].

As winter advances the newts gradually work their way closer to the stream, which they begin to enter in late February or early March after subsidence of the winter floods. Mating and spawning is mostly completed by early April, providing these activities are not interrupted too frequently by rains and consequent flooding. By May virtually all animals have left the stream, not to be seen again until the following autumn. In the intervening period, *rivularis,* unlike the more aquatic *granulosa* that inhabit the same streams, are almost as scarce as hen's teeth.

During the season when *rivularis* is in the water we maintain an almost continuous "hip-boot patrol" of the experimental stretch to record the locations of marked animals and to look for hybrids that may have finally matured and chosen to reward us with a return visit. This daily clamber through the icy waters, with its constant stooping to grasp our prey or to grope for them with numbed fingers beneath boulders or undercut banks, can hardly be characterized as a sophisticated scientific exercise. We are usually tired enough by dinnertime to confine our evenings to record-keeping, cards, or conversation, but night patrols with Coleman lanterns and flashlights are not uncommon, and are often highly profitable. The animals are less secretive than in the daylight hours, and we can reap a large harvest with less effort. After twelve years we have come to feel almost as much at home in Pepperwood Creek as the creatures we are searching for. Although I concede that it seems odd, we are always impatient for the next breeding season to arrive so that we can begin the same exhausting routine all over again.

EIGHT LITTLE FINGERS AND TEN LITTLE TOES

The reader has probably wondered how we give identifying marks to the newts, and I raise this point with some hesitation. I am fond of newts, and have no wish to cause them any discomfort, but the fact is that the only feasible and effective marking method we have been able to come up with is to snip off toes or larger portions of their appendages. Actually, judging from the newts' apparent unconcern, this is not a very traumatic experience for them, even if a whole foot is amputated; they soon go about their business again, including mating.

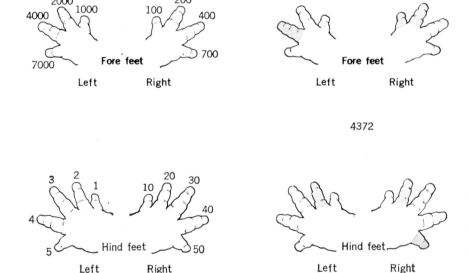

FIGURE 39. *The system of coding used to mark individual animals for recognition on subsequent capture. A: Key to the coding. B: Shaded toes would be clipped to specify individual 4372. Although the toes regenerate they remain recognizably smaller than normal toes for a period of several years.*

The advantage of toe clipping is that large numbers of animals can be given individually distinguishable markings. The coding system used is shown in Figure 39. When we first began the Pepperwood Creek project the size of the breeding population seemed so formidable that we thought more major, conspicuous amputations would be necessary. The prospect of picking up and examining every one of the thousands of newts we would encounter each day throughout the season, to see whether a big toe or index finger might be missing, appeared to be entirely prohibitive in terms of time and backaches. We might as well have resigned ourselves to this task at the outset, for it is precisely what we found we have to do.

Salamanders have the remarkable and unique capacity, among adult backboned animals, of growing new legs after they have been amputated. In some newts, including the species common in the eastern United States, the process of regeneration proceeds so rapidly that within a year or less an amputated leg reaches full size and is indistinguishable from the one it has replaced. If this were true of legs or digits of western newts I suspect that our homing studies, especially on their present extensive scale, might not have been feasible. Fortunately these fine animals are more accommodating than other newts, and regenerated parts, whether leg, foot, or digit, remain unmistakably smaller than normal for at least several years. As we shall see, however, their reduced size seems in no way to impede the newts as they make their almost incredibly long journeys.

No Place Like Home

The fidelity of newts—at least to the *places* where they breed—can no longer be questioned. Groups marked during the early years of the project have been returning ever since, with almost monotonous accuracy [78, 79], to the same portions of the experimental stretch where they were originally collected. I do not mean that there are no exceptions to this or that the accuracy is perfect. In each group we find nonconformists who choose to share their genes with neighbors in the next block, so to speak, and a very few venturesome ones who distribute their favors considerably farther afield. But generally speaking a group of animals found breeding in a given part of the stream in one year will still be returning there ten or twelve years later and presumably throughout their rather surprisingly long lifetimes.

A measure of their fidelity—and infidelity—is provided by Figure 40, showing the locations of recaptures in the largest single group that we have marked. All of these were originally captured in the fifty-yard stretch of stream constitut-

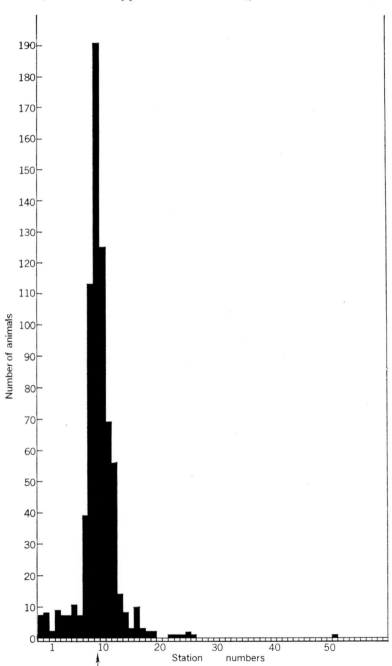

FIGURE 40. *During the years 1955 through 1960 all males entering the 50-yard stretch of Pepperwood Creek constituting Station 9 (arrow) were*

ing Station 9. Beginning in 1955, and continuing through 1960, this segment of water was intensively patrolled each day throughout the breeding seasons, and all males were marked by amputation of the right hind foot. Literally no stone was left unturned in our daily search, and certain crafty members of our crew became expert in timing their assigned patrols of other sections of the experimental stretch so that other members would arrive first for the tedious and tiring job of "doing Station 9." By 1960, when we had finally marked a grand total of almost two-thousand animals, the number of intact right feet entering this station had become very thin indeed. The histogram just cited shows the locations of recaptures made during the breeding season of 1964.

An even more impressive example of long-term identification with a specific portion of the breeding stream is provided by the series represented in Figure 41. All of the members of this group were first marked in 1955, and many are still being captured each year, almost without exception in the same part of the experimental stretch (Stations 1 through 8) where they were first collected. Additional series, marked in other portions of the stream, all conform to the same pattern, leading us to think of the population of the experimental stretch as being a mosaic of separate subpopulations. As we wade the length of the stretch, it has become so predictable where we shall encounter members of a given series that we are almost grateful for the excitement when we find exceptions—as we rarely do.

The evidence is thus clear that newts do return to the same breeding sites over the years, instead of selecting various ones at random. It is equally clear that any deviations from this rule are almost entirely limited to the home stream, and that breeding forays to other streams in the area virtually never occur. Since the project began in 1953, we have given identifying marks to well over twenty-thousand resident members of the experimental-stretch population, and only a single one of these has ever been found in a neighboring stream, although both this one, Danfield Creek, and the other adjoining one, Jim Creek, are patrolled fairly frequently and intensively. Apparently, then, we need not have worried about losing track of the hybrid embryos we released in the experimental stretch; if the behavior of their *rivularis* parents can be trusted as an indication, they would not be likely to scatter beyond our reach.

given a distinctive marking and released at Station 9. This histogram shows the numbers (totaling 712) and locations of these marked newts captured in the stream during the breeding season of 1964. The great majority of captures have been made each year at or near Station 9, but some animals have been captured both upstream and downstream from here. The two unnumbered stations upstream from Station 1 represent short stretches of the two tributaries just before they join to form Pepperwood Creek. (See aerial photograph, Fig. 38.)

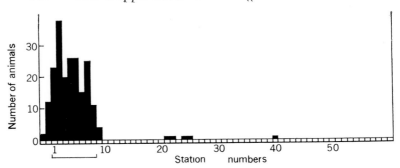

FIGURE 41. *Histogram showing recaptures (totaling 209) in 1964 of animals first marked at Stations 1 through 8, and released at Station 4, in 1955.*

These simple findings with marked newts immediately raised a number of questions that had nothing to do with the hybridization program. For example, do newts enter the same part of the stream for successive breedings merely because it is nearest to their terrestrial retreats? Or do they make a more significant choice, through recognition of distinctive sensory information that they associate with the breeding area? The obvious test is to displace animals from their accustomed segment of the stream to a foreign one, to see if they accept this new home or undertake to find their old one. These displacements have been made for various distances, and the results leave no doubts about the home-loving nature and navigational genius of California newts. Of the several series that we have tested, I shall describe only a few representative ones, all involving displacements for distances that must be considered great for animals as small and slow-moving as newts. I have made no careful clockings of a newt's speed, but if the reader compares it in his mind to that of a tortoise out for a leisurely stroll, he will not be far off.

The Long Trek Home

During the 1960 breeding season 564 male *rivularis* collected from the upper portion of the experimental stretch were released near its extreme lower end, a straight-line distance of almost exactly one mile [80]. Sixty-five percent of these have been recaptured during the ensuing years, and the great majority in precisely the part of the stream from which they had been displaced (see Fig. 42). A few of the newts failed to make the homing journey, and instead adopted, at least temporarily, the part of the stream where they were released. Homing seems to be an all-or-none phenomenon: the animals either accept the release site—as they seldom do—or, once initiating the return journey, refuse to stop short of its completion. Virtually no recaptures were made in the long stretch of stream intervening between the release and home sites. Incidentally, the route taken by the homing animals is almost entirely on land, along the mountainside, not in the stream channel itself. The extreme roughness of the terrain, cut at frequent intervals by deep gullies, makes the homing journey all the more difficult and accordingly all the more impressive.

It is of considerable incidental interest that displaced *rivularis* tend to emerge from their underground summer retreats earlier than do most non-displaced animals. This is clearly noticeable in the high percentage of displaced animals among those captured in our land traps just after the first autumn rains. They are apparently restless and anxious to be on their way to their proper homes. This homing "drive" is also manifested in the spring, in the weeks immediately following their displacement; recaptures of displaced animals in the traps continue decidedly later into the spring than do those of non-displaced ones, even though the peril of desiccation increases greatly with the seasonal cessation or decline in rainfall.

How far can newts be displaced without overtaxing their homing capacities? The limits have not yet been fully ascertained, but each year's experiments bring new evidence of their ability to navigate accurately over surprising dis-

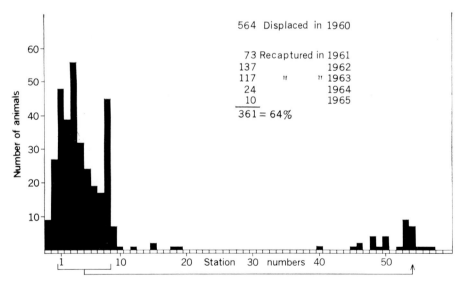

FIGURE 42. *Recaptures of animals displaced in 1960 from Stations 1 through 8 downstream to Station 54, a straight-line distance of one mile.*

tances and in the face of forbidding obstacles. This evidence comes from homing returns following transfer of animals from Pepperwood Creek to Jim and
Danfield Creeks [80], and also between these last two streams.

In 1960 a large group of newts was displaced from the lower portion of the
experimental stretch to a point deep in the canyon of upper Jim Creek, separated from Pepperwood by a mountain ridge rising about a thousand feet between them. The distance between collection and release sites is 1.35 miles
"as the crow flies," and certainly no less than two miles "as the newt crawls"
across the rugged intervening mountain. I was somewhat dubious about the
prospects of seeing these newts again, but, as Figure 43 shows, both the accuracy and the high percentage (81 percent) of returns were remarkable. Because of the profusion in which these animals poured back into the experimental stretch during the first three years following their displacement, we were
fearful lest eventually the recaptures would exceed 100 percent—which would
have been embarrassing! More recent returns have dwindled to a trickle, and
our concern has now vanished.

Almost equally decisive results have been obtained following displacements
from the experimental stretch to upper Danfield Creek (arrow on aerial photograph, Fig. 38), about three miles across the tortuous terrain separating it
from Pepperwood. In both this and the Jim Creek series the return migrations
were made on land, across the mountain ridges, not by the simple (but improbable) expedient of following Jim or Pepperwood Creeks down to their confluence with Pepperwood and thence upstream to the home segments. I shall
deal more specifically with this issue later.

The reader will have noted that the recaptures in these series were distributed over four or five years. This does not mean that those recovered most
recently necessarily waited longer before starting back, or took longer to make
the trip. As mentioned earlier, newts may not enter the stream for breeding
every year, and accordingly may not be detected in the home segment of stream
for a year or more after they have returned to its vicinity. We know this from
captures made, in land traps located at the home area, of animals that homed
the first year, but waited another year or more before entering the water.

However—and this is important—some animals do indeed linger at the displacement site for a year or more before beginning the homing journey, and
these exceptions are of especial interest. We have paid particular attention to
this point in the series displaced to Danfield Creek, since this stream is bordered
by a road and can thus be visited more frequently than the very inaccessible
part of Jim Creek where animals were released. Several members of the Danfield series were found in that stream at the beginning of the next season fol-

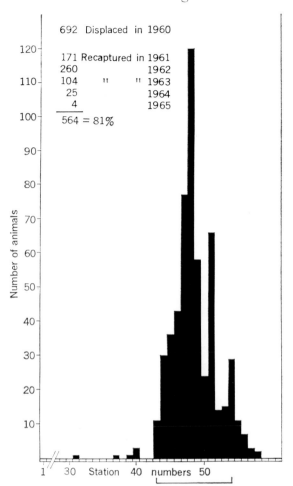

FIGURE 43. *Recaptures of animals displaced in 1960 from Stations 43 through 54 of Pepperwood Creek to the upper portion of Jim Creek, a distance of about two miles across the high mountain ridge separating the two streams. (See aerial photograph, Fig. 38.)*

lowing their displacement there, and were given individual toe markings. Two of them were found back in the experimental stretch before the end of this same season, and we have records of others that waited until the second or even third years before initiating and completing the return trip to Pepperwood Creek. This shows that memory of the home area and the ability to find it are very persistent faculties indeed.

The Longest Trek of All

The most demanding test of homing ability to which we have subjected *rivularis* began in 1963 when we displaced 730 males approximately five miles, from Danfield Creek to Jim Creek. The animals were taken from a 0.4-mile stretch of Danfield Creek extending downstream from the release site in the series just referred to above, and deposited at the same place in Jim Creek to which the series from Pepperwood was displaced.

This series is of especial interest not only because of the long distances involved, but because of other aspects of homing behavior that it illuminates. One of these is the course followed by homing animals. As mentioned in the description of the shorter displacements, the route followed is an overland one. The evidence concerning this point is particularly clear from the present series, and is heightened in interest by the fact that a third stream, Pepperwood Creek, intervenes between the stream in which the animals were released and the one from which they were collected. Partly for special purposes to be mentioned later, "land traps" have been installed at numerous sites in the study area (Fig. 44). These are low wire-mesh ("hardware cloth") fences that funnel migrating newts into escape-proof cages, and are of great help in gaining information about their terrestrial movements. Several of the traps are situated along the experimental stretch, and another series is located high on the ridge separating Jim and Pepperwood Creeks. The locations of the traps, together with data on recaptures in the Danfield-to-Jim Creek series, are shown in Figure 45.

The displacements were made during March, 1963, and no captures were made in the traps until the following fall; as mentioned earlier, *rivularis* does not move about during the dry months between late spring and autumn. But in November and December, after the first heavy rains, animals began to show up in the traps on the ridge, and before spring a total of 48 was captured in these fences. Following the first captures in the ridge traps, members of the series began to be intercepted in the traps along the experimental stretch, and during the winter and spring 60 were caught in these traps and in the stretch itself. During the same season 28 members were recaptured in the home creek, Danfield, all of them in the section from which they had been removed the year before.

During the following year, 12 animals, a smaller number than the year before, were caught in the ridge traps. This confirms a conclusion we had formulated earlier, namely, that a majority of animals tend to initiate the homing journey the first year following displacement. An additional 70 were found

FIGURE 44. *Same aerial photograph as Figure 38, marked to show locations of wire-mesh "fences" designed to capture animals migrating on land after displacement from one portion to another of Pepperwood Creek or from Pepperwood and Danfield Creeks to Jim Creek. Fences are indicated by white lines adjacent to Pepperwood Creek and on the ridge overlooking Jim Creek.*

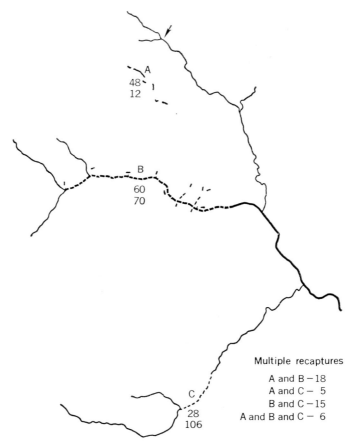

FIGURE 45. *Recaptures of animals en route home after displacement from upper Danfield Creek (portion indicated by broken line) to upper Jim Creek (arrow). A: Captures in traps on the ridge separating Jim and Pepperwood Creeks; B: in the traps along the experimental stretch of Pepperwood Creek or in the stream itself; and C: in the portion of Danfield Creek from which the animals were originally collected for displacement. In each of the three locations the number of animals captured the first year following displacement (1963–64) is shown above, and those captured the second year (1964–65) is shown below. The numbers of dual or triple captures of the same animals at these three locations are summarized in the lower right-hand corner.*

along the experimental stretch, and 106 more made it all the way back to the home stretch of Danfield Creek. There is no question in our minds that another substantial haul will be made here in 1966—of animals which at the time of writing are holed-up underground at various places en route while waiting for the rains to set them on their way again. The percentage already accounted for, at home or en route there, is already about 40 percent of the total displaced, and I shall not be surprised if after another year it is considerably higher.

Clearly, then, the animals in this series are following a fairly direct overland route on their way home, not the more circuitous water-passage down Jim Creek and then up Danfield Creek. In fact, no members of the series have been found in the lower part of Jim Creek, in Pepperwood Creek below the experimental stretch, or in the long portion of Danfield Creek below the segment of the stream where the series was originally collected.

I did not anticipate, frankly, that we would capture as many animals as we have in the land traps. They are so widely spaced, and screen the homeward route so incompletely, that they can intercept only a small percentage of the animals moving in this general direction. The probability that a given animal will be intercepted at more than one point along the route is very low. However, several double or triple captures were made, and these are summarized in the lower right-hand corner of Figure 45. The designations A, B, and C refer to captures in the ridge traps, along the experimental stretch, and in the home stretch of Danfield Creek, respectively. Figure 46 shows the mountain ridges traversed by the homing animals.

In returning home from Jim Creek the newts in this series must ford the intervening stream, Pepperwood Creek, and one wonders if some of them might not stop there and adopt it as their new home. Only time will provide the answer, but it is already clear that several animals have at least wavered in their loyalty to Danfield Creek. Specifically, our records show that of the 60 members of the series captured in or along the experimental stretch during the first year following displacement, 16 were found there again during the 1965 breeding season. My prediction is that by 1966 some of these will have moved on to Danfield Creek, but that others may linger in Pepperwood Creek for a longer time, or maybe even permanently.

Another interesting feature of this series is the clear implication that the homing journey is not prompted solely by the urge to breed. Some of the males captured en route home, for example in the traps along the experimental stretch, showed no development whatever of the secondary sexual characteristics always associated with impending breeding activity. Dissection of a few such animals showed that the testes were undeveloped, confirming that no breeding was scheduled for at least another year. It seems clear, therefore, that hormonal factors associated with breeding are not involved in the motivation or "release" of homing activity. To newts, then, home seemingly means "the right place to

FIGURE 46. *Pepperwood Valley is in the center. Danfield Creek courses beyond the mountain ridge to the left, and Jim Creek beyond the ridge to the right. Thus the animals displaced from Danfield Creek to Jim Creek had to cross both of these mountains and the intervening Pepperwood*

live," not merely the "right place to breed." However, more information about this issue is needed before final conclusions can be drawn.

New and Narrow Paths

When one displaces an animal, whether bird, newt, or unwanted housecat, from point A to point B, and finds that it returns to A, certain standard questions always arise. If I had known how difficult it is to find the answers to some of these questions, I might have been inclined to stay with experimental embryology, or possibly to turn to something easy, such as biophysics. Almost invariably the first question I am asked by anyone hearing of our work with newts is "How do they do it?" meaning, "Do the animals see, smell, hear, or feel their way home?" I have even been asked if I think there may be a system of tunnels connecting Jim, Pepperwood, and Danfield Creeks! If one is interested

Creek and Valley. The lake to the left may be used as a reference point in relating the topography in this photograph to that shown in the aerial photograph, Figure 38.

in the broader aspects of homing, and not merely in its sensory physiology, then there are other questions that are of at least equal importance. Even the distance is of crucial significance, since it is one thing for an animal to see, smell, or feel its way home after displacement for a few hundred yards, and quite another for it to navigate for several miles by one or more of these special senses.

The present section will deal with two other questions important to the interpretation of homing behavior: (1) whether the displaced newts may have had previous acquaintance with the sites where they were released, and thus may have possessed information that would help them get their bearings; and (2) whether they find the home area by oriented migration, or by a meandering search that might eventually lead them to their destination merely through chance. I have already touched by implication on these questions and possible answers in the preceding pages, but they will now be given more explicit consideration.

As for the dependence of homing upon previous familiarity with the release site, I think the answer can be a categorical "no." We have seen, for example, that animals displaced from the upper portion (Stations 1 through 8) to the extreme lower part of the experimental stretch (Station 54) can home very successfully. But another series cited, the group marked in the same stretch and left there (Fig. 41), shows that animals native to this upper part of the stream virtually never visit other parts and hence could not have acquainted themselves with the remote stream segment from which their displaced associates homed so readily. The large group of almost two thousand *rivularis* marked at Station 9 supports the same conclusion (Fig. 40). Although in subsequent years they dispersed moderate distances both upstream and downstream from Station 9, only a single member of the series has ever been found downstream as far as Station 54, in all of the patrols that we have made since the series was initiated over ten years ago.

We can also say with assurance that animals native to the upper portion of the experimental stretch almost never, in the course of their normal terrestrial excursions between successive breeding seasons, wander far enough in a downstream direction to encounter and familiarize themselves with hillside points overlooking the lower part of the stretch. This conclusion is based on the distribution of captures in the land traps situated along the experimental stretch. With very rare exceptions the animals caught in these traps are those that breed in nearby segments of the stream. The fact that animals do not wander far enough laterally on the mountainsides to acquire knowledge of the terrain overlooking both ends of the experimental stretch is particularly clear from captures in one of the traps at the crest of the ridge between the experimental stretch and Jim Creek. During the fall and winter seasons of 1961–62 and 1962–63, 96 *rivularis* captured in the trap directly uphill from about Station 30 were given a distinctive toe clipping. We have since captured 49 of these animals in our patrols of the experimental stretch, and although they were distributed over a considerable length of the stretch, only one was encountered upstream from Station 20. Conversely, not one of the almost two thousand animals marked at Station 9 has ever been found in the ridge traps. The general picture presented by these and other observations is that as animals move uphill from their native segments of the stream, they fan out over a gradually widening area, but that even at the crest of the watershed their lateral dispersion is never by any means great enough to acquaint them with the full extent of the ridge overlooking the experimental stretch.

It is also highly improbable that familiarity with distant areas is gained by migrations during juvenile stages, since *rivularis* seems to engage in very limited movements until the approach of maturity. This judgment is based partly on the remarkably small number of juveniles captured in the land traps.

We can thus safely assume that the very great majority of animals that homed after displacement for the full length of the experimental stretch could not have relied on any previous acquaintance with the release site or even with its near vicinity. The evidence is even more incontrovertible for the groups displaced to foreign streams. As mentioned earlier, only a single member of the resident experimental-stretch population, out of over twenty thousand marked since the project began, has been found in either of the two neighboring streams. But if any lingering doubt remains, it must be dispelled by the highly successful homing of animals displaced from Danfield to Jim Creek. If animals rarely visit back and forth between adjoining streams, think how unlikely it is that they ever infiltrate the domains of more distant populations, separated from their own by an intervening stream and its native inhabitants.

ORIENTED MIGRATION OR RANDOM SEARCH?

Granting, then, that the animals displaced in these studies found themselves in entirely foreign territory, did they then begin a random search for familiar settings, or was there some long-distance perception of navigational cues that enabled them to orient their migrations in the proper directions at the outset of homing? Evidence of various kinds points clearly to the latter alternative.

Our first tests of orientation were performed with a special enclosure designated as the "star-trap" [78] because of its shape (Fig. 47). It was constructed near the streamside, about midway along the experimental stretch. At the tip of each arm of the enclosure there was an opening into an escape-proof cage, and in the center was a box from which animals could escape at their leisure by a spiral ramp leading to an opening in the lid. Animals collected from upstream or downstream portions of the creek were placed in the box during late afternoon or early evening, and the cages were checked the following morning to see whether the animals had moved toward or away from their home sites. The results showed that animals taken from the water at moderate distances (about 50 to 400 yards) either upstream or downstream oriented in the direction of home in a very conclusive majority of cases [79]. Virtually without exception, tests of animals from upstream and downstream sites were conducted simultaneously, using toe clipping to distinguish the two groups. This assures that the comparisons were made under identical meteorological and other environmental conditions. (The animals from upstream used in these and other

FIGURE 47. *"Star-trap." A star-shaped enclosure, with an escape-proof cage at the tip of each arm, designed to test the ability of newts to orient their movements after being transferred to the enclosure from other locations. The enclosure is situated near the breeding stream (arrow indicates direction of stream flow). Animals to be tested are collected from upstream or downstream locations and placed in the release box in the center of the enclosure (pictured in the photograph inset in the left-hand corner). From Twitty [78].*

tests were usually unmarked, while those from downstream were deprived of the fourth digit on the right front foot. As a consequence, the segments of stream immediately downstream from the star-trap are to this day poor collecting territory for animals that we wish to toe-clip serially for other displacement experiments; scores of the animals must be screened to find a few with this digit still intact. If additional evidence of loyalty to home territory were needed, the animals in this part of the stream would provide it in abundance.)

If animals taken from greater distances up- or downstream were tested in the star-trap, evidence of orientation diminished or disappeared. At first I interpreted this to indicate that animals displaced for these longer distances had to rely upon random search to bring them within hailing distance of the home territory, after which they could begin to pick up signals that would enable them to zero in for the final leg of the journey. There was, however, another possibility: namely, that the test enclosure was so small that the animals became trapped in one of its cages before there was enough time to probe for and detect the direction of weakened signals coming from afar, such as the greatly diluted odors that might emanate from the vegetation of the home area. Why not, then, build a bigger and better star-trap, so that animals could move about more freely, waiting for the weaker clues to register on their senses before their explorations led them to premature capture in a "wrong" cage? This we proceeded to do, but in locating the new enclosure we failed to take certain important considerations into account. The area enclosed by the fence was partly open meadow and partly dense forest. When released in foreign situations offering a sharp choice between exposure and concealment, a newt's first instinct is to head for a dark horizon and the surer promise of protection that it offers. This can be confirmed simply by emptying a bucketful of newts in the open and watching them crawl concertedly toward a nearby cluster of trees or even a large fallen log. We assume this is the reason most of the captures were made in cages situated within the wooded portion of the large enclosure, regardless of the direction of the home segment of stream. But the enclosure, which we call the "macrotron" because of its size, has proven useful for other purposes, and accordingly we do not bemoan the labor that went into its construction. (We have adopted shorthand designations for other test facilities. A large shed built for special orientation tests soon became the "newtron," and a smaller one the "newtrino.")

Since the star-trap was too small, and the macrotron ill-designed, for tests of orientation following long-distance displacements, we turned to a somewhat different approach to the problem. This involved the displacement of animals from one part of Pepperwood Creek to another, releasing them midway between two series of land traps situated about three hundred yards apart. When the animals dispersed from the stream, the distribution of their captures in the two sets of traps would tell us whether they were scattering at random or moving primarily in the direction of home. The locations of the two trap series, extending transversely to the stream at Stations 43 and 49 are indicated on Figure 44 (see Fig. 38 for station numbers), and their design is shown in Figure 48.

One group of animals released midway between the trap series was collected from upstream locations, and a second was taken from a remote point downstream in Pepperwood Creek, above the confluence of Danfield Creek. A third series was taken from lower portions of the experimental stretch and released half-way between land traps situated near Stations 1 and 9.

FIGURE 48. *A "drift fence" extending at right angles to the breeding stream and designed to capture animals moving in an up- or downstream direction. Escape-proof cages are situated near each end of the fence, and partitions in the cages make it possible to determine whether an animal was moving upstream or downstream at the time of interception. Photograph by David Grant.*

The recaptures in the three series, made as the displaced animals left the water at the end of the breeding season and were intercepted in the land traps, are shown schematically in Figure 49. In each series the number of animals caught in the homeward direction greatly exceeded that in the opposite direction, showing that there is indeed a strong tendency toward initial orientation

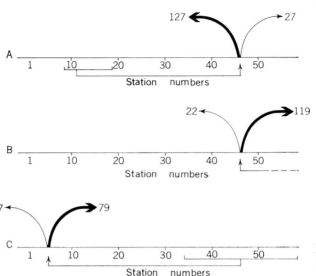

FIGURE 49. *When newts are displaced upstream or downstream, and released mid-way between "drift fences" (Fig. 48) situated near the streamside, the great majority of them are captured in the fences situated in the direc-tion of home. See aerial photograph (Fig. 44) for locations of drift fences. A: 715 animals were displaced from Stations 9 through 19 downstream to Station 46. B: 617 animals were displaced from near the junction of Danfield Creek (see aerial photograph, Fig. 38) up-stream to Station 46. C: 538 animals were displaced from Stations 34 through 58 upstream to Station 5.*

following displacement for major distances.* Since the animals were marked serially, by coded toe clipping, individual case histories are being accumulated that will be of increasing interest as further captures are made in other traps along the experimental stretch and in the stream itself during subsequent breed-ing seasons. For example, we have already found animals that first moved in the "wrong" direction, but subsequently corrected their orientation and began to travel toward home.

---

* Two large additional series of animals released midway between the trap series at Stations 43 and 49 during the 1966 breeding season showed that initial orientation occurs after displacement for much greater straight-line distances than those involved here. Both new series were displaced from the downstream direction, one from three miles away in lower Pepperwood Creek, and the other from eight miles away in another stream. (Actual overland distances in the mountainous terrain intervening between the collection and re-lease sites are, of course, much greater). In both series subsequent trap captures during the remainder of the spring showed a high degree of initial orientation in the homeward direction!

"NONSENSE" ORIENTATION—AN UNEXPECTED OBSERVATION

Before leaving these tests on homing orientation I should like to mention an entirely unexpected phenomenon that turned up during their conduct. As already explained in the legend for Figure 48, the two series of traps near Stations 43 and 49 were so designed that we could determine whether at the time of capture an animal was moving in an upstream or downstream direction. Several other traps along the experimental stretch are constructed on the same principle. This design was adopted primarily to follow the movements of displaced animals, but during the first year following the installation of these traps, we began to note an odd feature of the capture of nondisplaced members of the population. Specifically, many more animals were moving in a general upstream direction at the time of capture than were moving downstream. This difference first caught our attention toward the end of the breeding season, at a time when the animals were beginning to leave the stream and move uphill following mating and spawning. Accordingly, in all subsequent examinations of the traps we have made careful records of the numbers of nondisplaced animals captured while moving in the two directions.

Records covering the period from late March, 1963, to the present time show a rather clear picture. Each spring, after the breeding season is well advanced or nearing completion, the great majority of the captures are made in the downstream sides of the traps, showing that the animals were moving in an upstream direction at the time of interception. During the summer there is a complete hiatus in these captures, since no animals are moving during the dry period of the year. Following the resumption of capture the next fall, the percentages of animals found in the upstream and downstream sides of the traps are approximately equal.

The explanation of this behavior is obscure. Since the predominance of upstream migration is particularly conspicuous during the period when the animals are leaving the water following the breeding season, one might suggest that the phenomenon is a compensation for any downstream displacements to which the animals might have been subjected through the force of the current. However, our observations on individually marked animals during the course of the breeding season provide little support for this interpretation. Repeated captures of the same animals during the course of the season show little if any evidence of any major downstream displacements.

It is not inconceivable, however, that the stream current operates in another way to influence the orientation of an animal following its departure from the stream. While in the water, the animals show a conspicuous tendency to face into the current and, in fact, often to progress upstream against it. (In this way they possibly compensate for any minor downstream displacements they may experience; for example, when they are at the mercy of the current during mating.) In situations where the animals are unable to breast the current successfully, for example, at points in the stream where the channel narrows abruptly, it is not uncommon to see the animals leave the water and reenter it upstream after a short excursion along the bank. When the animals leave the water toward the end of the breeding season for lengthier uphill excursions on land, it is conceivable that the upstream component of their terrestrial movements is an extrapolation of their earlier orientation to the current.

Possible support for this interpretation comes from the distribution of captures in the upstream and downstream sides of the traps of newly metamorphosed frogs (*Rana boylii*) following the first rains in the autumn. During this season of the year *rivularis,* which have not been in the water since the preceding spring, are captured in approximately equal numbers in both sides of the traps, whereas the young frogs, which have just recently emerged from the streams, are captured in the downstream sides in percentages even greater than those characteristic of adult newts at the end of the spring breeding season.

Whatever the explanation of the phenomenon may be, it has an obvious bearing on the use of land traps in investigating initial orientation of newts following displacement. If animals indeed have a tendency to move in an upstream direction on leaving the water, then the upstream movements of newts that have been displaced downstream might be nothing more than a reflection of this tendency, and not necessarily a manifestation of true homing orientation. Fortunately, our results enabled us to discount this complication, since we had already discovered that displaced newts move predominantly in the direction of home whether they have been displaced upstream or downstream (Fig. 49). We must conclude, then, that homing orientation is a stronger "drive" than the tendency for upstream movement, and overwhelms or dominates the latter when the two are in conflict.

If any final evidence may be needed to clinch the conclusion that newts do not return to the home area merely by random search, it is provided by the Danfield-to-Jim Creek displacements. If the newts in this series had been prone to radiate aimlessly in all directions from the release site in upper Jim Creek, the probabilities are negligible that we would have recaptured such a large percentage of them in the remote and restricted home segment of Danfield Creek or at way points en route to this destination. I do not mean, of course, that displaced newts follow the straightest possible "beeline" in returning home, or that there are never vagrant moments en route when they may even stray temporarily in quite false directions, but there can be no doubt that there is usually a strong element of orientation that carries them predominantly toward their proper destination.

A few friends have expressed skepticism about the ability of newts to perform the homing feats that I have reported. I can sympathize with this attitude, because I too had never thought of these animals' intellects in flattering terms. But I assure any doubters that to the best of my knowledge and ability the reports are honest and accurate. Even if I were tempted to embellish the story, for purposes of effect, I would be frustrated by the watchful and unyielding integrity of the assistants and students who have worked closely with me on all phases of the program.

These worthy collaborators have not only guarded my veracity, they have made the Pepperwood Creek Affair possible through their able participation. In all kinds of weather—and the California coastal ranges can provide quite an assortment—a succession of them have shared the diversified chores of constructing and maintaining the numerous facilities essential to the operation of a modern newt ranch, and of riding endless herd on its far-flung denizens. Antone Jacobsen, Gilbert Church, Man Chiang Niu, William Brandom, Wayne Packer, James Duncan, William Davis, and Herbert Little were among the earlier members of the changing crew, and Thomas Algard, Douglas Kelly, and Duane Heath lent helpful hands on a few occasions. During the past few years David Grant and Oscar Anderson have been especially indispensable contributors to the enterprise. To all of these; to the Radtkey family that manages El Rancho Seto Sendero; to its original owner, Roy Hedgpeth, and its present one, James Soper; and by no means least of all to the National Science Foundation for financial support of the project, I am greatly indebted. And lest there be domestic repercussions, perhaps I should acknowledge the culinary services and genial company afforded us by my wife in her capacity as resident cook and domino expert during the busy spring season at the ranch.

Nor Sight Nor Feel Nor Sound

It seems clear from the preceding section that animals finding themselves in foreign territory somehow "get a message" signaling the general direction of their home territory, even after displacement for major distances. What is the nature of this message? In a paper written in 1959 [78] I emphasized some of the difficulties encountered in attacking this question, and suggested that if we did not soon find the answer it would perhaps be expedient to turn the whole problem over to the Stanford chaplain for assignment to one of his divinity majors.

Possibly this was not such a bad idea after all, since at the time of this writing, six years later, we are still not quite ready to make a final deposition concerning the sensory basis of newt homing behavior. However, we have continued to plug away at the problem, and are at least in a stronger position than before to hazard some fairly sound guesses.

In surveying the various senses for likely candidates, one thinks first of sight, since visual reference to terrestrial landmarks or celestial bodies is so important in the homing activities of certain other animals. Our most direct and significant tests of vision have been made with three groups of newts that were displaced after being blinded permanently by the surgical removal of both eyes.

The first series was displaced from the upper end of the experimental stretch downstream to Station 20, a straight-line distance of approximately one-quarter mile [78, 79]. Considering that one hind limb was also removed to facilitate ready recognition of the animals, I was not too sanguine about the survival of these handicapped creatures, much less about their ability to home successfully. However, ten percent of the members of the series were recaptured the next breeding season (Fig. 50), and a few more in subsequent years, all in the portion of the stream from which they had originally been collected. Of the countless displaced newts that I have handled, I think none has made such an impact on me as the first one of these blinded animals to be recaptured. As I examined its empty eye-sockets and emaciated body, and then looked downstream toward the heavy forest and rugged terrain it had traversed in coming home, my respect for its accomplishment came as near to awe and reverence as can be inspired by lowly organisms or possibly even by their highly evolved descendants.

Salamanders can survive long periods of starvation, and it was evident from the scrawny appearance of some of the recaptured animals that they had eaten little, perhaps nothing, since they had been blinded a year earlier. But this was not true of all the sightless newts, and one of the interesting by-products of the experiments has been the demonstration that vision is not as indispensable in the general economy of newts as one might think. Each spring we still recapture a few members of a series blinded ten years ago, and most of them are as plump and seemingly as healthy as the sighted newts in the same pools. Once having "made the grade," and no longer confronted with the hazards incidental to homing, they can apparently live the rest of their lives in harmony with their environment. Whether their other senses become sharpened—or even whether this kind of compensation is possible in salamanders—we do not know. It is biologically reasonable, however, that *rivularis* should be less dependent on vision than many other animals. In organisms living and feeding underground for a major part of their lives, and foraging mostly at night when

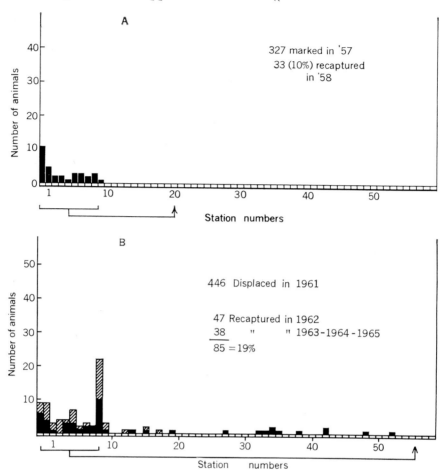

FIGURE 50. Histograms showing successful homing of animals permanently blinded by surgical removal of the eyes. A: Recaptures of animals displaced downstream for a straight-line distance of approximately ¼ mile. B: Recaptures of animals displaced downstream for a straight-line distance of approximately one mile. Animals captured the first year following displacement are represented by black bars, and those captured subsequently by diagonally striped bars.

not in hiding, it is not entirely surprising that vision is a less crucial sense than one might otherwise be led to expect by their possession of large and well-developed eyes.

Sightlessness nevertheless takes its toll, especially when blinded animals are displaced for great distances. In 1961 we transferred a second series of blinded *rivularis* from the upper portion of the experimental stretch to its extreme lower end. (Unlike the series just described, these animals were not subjected to limb markings, since our practice during more recent years of picking up and scrutinizing closely all newts encountered during the stream patrols obviates the necessity of conspicuous markings.) Although the percentage of recaptures is substantial, it is considerably lower than in the series of sighted newts subjected to the same displacement (Fig. 42). The majority of the blinded animals recaptured in the first year following displacement were concentrated in the home segment of stream, but several entered the water at scattered points short of this objective (Fig. 50). I do not believe, however, that this reflects any primary dependence on vision as the means of locating or recognizing the home area. The physical condition of most of the blinded animals suggested instead that they had been handicapped in feeding, and that the resulting impairment of vigor militated against completion of the homing journey before the time that they were impelled by hormonally induced "water drive" to enter the stream for breeding. This interpretation is supported by the fact that all animals of the series captured in subsequent years, without exception, have been found in or close to the home segment itself. Whatever the explanation may be for the smaller percentage of recaptures and the somewhat lower accuracy of the first year's returns, the fact remains that this second series did a very creditable job of homing and thus established beyond question that vision is not a highly critical sense in newt navigation. I do not mean to imply that it is not utilized at all in homing. Ferguson [81, 82] has shown that frogs can use the sun as a compass for purposes of orientation, and I should not be greatly surprised if similarly conducted tests proved newts to have the same capacity. But if eyeless animals can home as effectively as they do following displacement for a distance of one mile, it seems clear that we must look elsewhere for the primary source of navigational information.

The third series of blinded *rivularis*, also displaced in 1961, was collected from Stations 12 through 20 and deposited in upper Jim Creek at the same site used for the release of the groups of sighted animals described earlier. Here the hazards associated with blindness are especially great, since in traversing the barren mountain slope rising from Jim Creek animals would be severely handicapped in finding cover when faced with adverse changes in temperature or humidity. As mentioned earlier, *rivularis* depends heavily on vision in seeking the sheltered niches advertised by dark or wooded horizons. We believe that mortalities resulting from blindness account for the small number of recaptures (34); even so, all of these, with one exception, were made in or very near the home portion of the experimental stretch.

As an alternative to vision, one of the first possibilities considered was that animals orient their movements and identify the home segment of stream, or

FIGURE 51. *"Table trap." A platform that may be adjusted to different heights and degrees of inclination, designed to test the ability of newts to orient their movements when crawling on an unfamiliar and artificial terrain. From Twitty [78].*

its bordering terrain, through "muscle memory." Any one of *us*, conceivably, if we tramped repeatedly over an area of irregular terrain, might become so familiar with its topography that we could subsequently recognize any given spot within the area and orient our route accordingly in any chosen direction —even if we were blinded. This would not be an effective device after displacement to remote and foreign areas, but it might help account for results such as those obtained in the star-trap with animals displaced for modest distances.

The possibility was tested by use of a large platform (30 by 6 feet), carpeted with polyethylene plastic sheeting, that could be adjusted at selected heights above the ground and tilted at different angles (Fig. 51). Mixed groups of animals, half from upstream locations and half from downstream, were placed in a release box at the center of the platform. Whether the platform was level or tilted, the animals sorted themselves out quite successfully, each group being captured predominantly in the cage at the end of the platform toward its home stretch of stream. Since the composition and topography of the terrain afforded by the platform were entirely new to the animals, it is clear that they were not orienting along its surface in response to any tactile or kinesthetic memories. We may thus infer that just as animals do not see their way home, neither do they feel their way home.

What are the possibilities that remain? I feel that hearing can be discounted, not only because salamanders are voiceless and hence make no calls to which displaced animals might respond, but also because the seasonal and yearly changes in stream sounds, resulting from fluctuating volume of flow and shifting configuration and course of the stream bed, would provide no reliable reference sounds.

Do They Smell Their Way Home?

In our search for navigational devices we are rapidly running out of senses, with olfaction or related chemical senses being the only orthodox candidate left to explore. Does this then mean that newts smell their way home, and when they get there does home—to them—mean a familiar and distinctive set of odors peculiar to the soil and vegetation along the streamside at that particular point? In animals as earthbound as salamanders, living throughout their terrestrial phase in such intimate association with humid soil and all its products, it is not unlikely that the odors of their environment loom larger in their experience than do impressions of sight and sound. We do know that these newts have a remarkable sense of smell. It is by means of scent that the *rivularis* males detect the presence and location of females when the latter enter the stream for breeding. A female, or even a sponge soaked in water in which females have been stored, dipped briefly in the stream will excite and attract males from many yards downstream (Fig. 52).

When we plugged the olfactory passages with petroleum jelly, as can be done very effectively by barely melting the jelly and then injecting it into the nasal openings, orientation did seem to disappear or become greatly reduced when the animals were tested in the star-trap [78]. In fact, most of the animals remained in the release box, refusing to migrate at all. However, the obstruction of the nasal passages also interferes with breathing, and we could not be sure that the effects on migration and orientation were not a result of the trauma caused by the difficulty in breathing rather than of the loss of the sense of smell.

FRUSTRATION AND CONFESSION

To avoid this complication, we constructed the special test enclosure which I referred to earlier as the "newtron." This was a many-doored shed (Fig. 53) about 40 by 9 feet, designed (we thought) to permit control of environmental factors such as light, and access and direction of flow of airborne odors. A gasoline-powered generator was installed nearby to operate a fan and electric bulbs, and also a pump that would bring water from the stream to regulate humidity. The platform mentioned earlier was moved into the shed so that

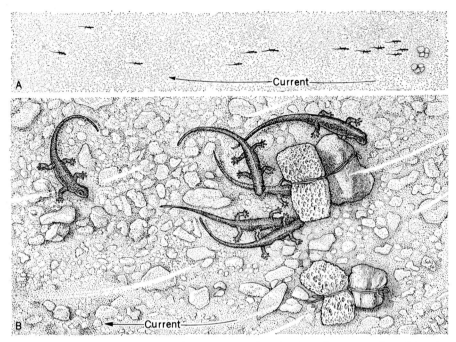

FIGURE 52. *Males are attracted upstream to females by substances released by the females. If a sponge is soaked in water in which females have been stored it attracts males from many yards downstream (A). They cluster around the sponge, investigating it closely, but ignore nearby sponges not bearing the female secretions (B). From Twitty [74].*

tests of orientation could be made either at or above the ground level. Altogether it was a laborious and not inexpensive construction job, built, as most of our outdoor facilities at the ranch seem to be, during cold and rainy weather. I confess with some reluctance that its main usefulness has proved to be as a shelter for sheep during the winter! I would not even reveal its existence, except to illustrate how research can be compounded of high hopes, hard work, disappointment, and naiveté. One possible cause of its failure as a device to study the subtleties of olfaction in newt orientation was the fact that for at least two years it stank to high Heaven of raw timbers and plywood. A little elementary knowledge of aerodynamics would have warned us that a fan would pull air through the shed in complex patterns and eddies instead of in the concerted unidirectional flow that we had fondly expected. The many hundreds of animals that we carried through the portals of the newtron must have been thoroughly bewildered by what they found there, for little if any sense could ever be made of the directions in which they moved or of their choice of nooks and corners—

where they gathered in confused desperation. Eventually the odors of the building subsided, but by then we had become so disillusioned that we avoided it with downcast eyes and, recently, were glad to have it dismantled and the lumber used to build a sheep shed elsewhere on the ranch.

Now that I am in a mood of confession, I might as well refer to another effort which, although more fertile than that involved in the newtron, nevertheless failed to advance greatly our knowledge of the sensory basis of homing. Since the star-trap had always served us so faithfully, we decided to adapt it for the purposes we had in mind when we constructed the newtron. This was done by covering it with a large tent of opaque plastic sheeting (Fig. 54) that would permit us to regulate the admission of airborne odors without conferring any smells of its own. When this tent was closed around its entire perimeter animals placed in the release box gave somewhat ambiguous responses. The following morning many of them were still wandering untrapped within the star-trap enclosure, perhaps suggesting that they were indeed handicapped in sensing environmental signals when sealed off from odor sources. However, there was still some evidence of orientation, especially in animals that had been collected from upstream locations. Of the upstream animals that were

FIGURE 53. *"Newtron." A building designed (unsuccessfully!) to test the ability of newts to orient the direction of their movements under conditions of controlled light and airflow.*

FIGURE 54. *The star-trap (Fig. 47) was enclosed by a tentlike covering of opaque plastic sheeting, for orientation tests similar to those for which the newtron was designed.*

trapped, a significant majority were consistently found in the cages of the arms pointing toward home, and the untrapped upstream ones were more numerous in the upstream half of the enclosure than in the downstream half. Oddly, however, animals from downstream locations were distributed either in approximately equal numbers in all cages or areas of the enclosure or at best in only slightly greater numbers in their homeward half. One might be tempted to suggest that when external sources of information are not available, the "nonsense" tendency toward upstream orientation mentioned earlier tends to assert itself and take control. But if this were the sole factor, animals from both upstream and downstream locations would be expected to behave identically. Since they clearly did not, it looks as if obscure external factors must have still been operating in spite of all our efforts to seal them off, but further speculation is clearly unprofitable at the present time.

When one end of the tent was left open, by supporting its margin about a foot above ground, the response was very striking. Animals moved toward this end in overwhelming numbers, and became trapped in the cages there, quite independently of whether this carried them in the direction of home or away from it. At first we thought this might be a response to airborne odors, entering at the open end from both up- and downstream sources. This idea was quickly dispelled by the next experiment. The margins of the tent were again closed around the entire perimeter, but now small windows were cut out of the black sheeting at one end of the tent and replaced by pieces of translucent plastic. The animals hastened to this end of the star-trap as concertedly as when there had been an opening there, showing that their response was to light, not to air or any odors it might transmit. This was further confirmed by constructing a light-trap at one end of the tent, thus excluding light but not air; the behavior of the animals was now the same as if the tent were completely sealed.

Since the only clear, unequivocal responses shown by animals in the star-trap tent were to light, and since our results with the displacement of blind animals show that vision is not the key sense in homing, the reader can perhaps understand why we have discontinued this approach to the analysis of orientation, at least for the time being. Our belief is that in the tent experiments we confronted a phenomenon that has plagued investigators before, namely, a "trap reaction" or "escape reaction" to abnormal confinement that obscures or overwhelms the behavior that the experiments are designed to investigate. (I would not be at all surprised, incidentally, that if we used a transparent tent with a black window or darkened recess at one end, the animals would respond to its offer of concealment or escape in precisely the same way that they were attracted to the light source in the opaque tent.) I do not doubt that better trained or cleverer students of animal behavior could design experimental facilities that would overcome these complications, but after the frustrations we have encountered, including some that I do not choose to expose, my present inclination is to believe that "it may not be easy." I am reminded of what has been referred to as the "Harvard first law of animal behavior." According to this dictum, the investigator sets up his experiment with meticulous care, controlling all factors rigorously so that his test subjects can give only clear and illuminating responses, "whereupon the animals do as they blankety-blank please."

BACK TO SURGERY

Almost from the beginning of our studies of homing I recognized that the most direct and effective means of testing the role of olfaction might be to destroy the sense of smell by surgical means. Several years ago, accordingly, I performed exploratory operations on a few preserved newts to ascertain the feasibility of destroying the olfactory nerves. Possibly because of the more brittle condition of the skull and other tissues after preservation, I gained the impression that the operative procedures would be too radical and traumatic. No further trials were made until a few years later, when David Grant found that the nerves of anaesthetized animals could be severed or removed with virtually no mortality or other serious consequences. After cutting a rectangular window in the roof of the skull, sections of the olfactory nerves are destroyed by pinching with fine-pointed forceps, and the wound is closed simply by replacing the flap of bone and skin that had been left attached at one end. With practice the entire operation can be performed in about three minutes, and in as little as a couple of hours the animals often recover sufficiently to resume feeding. Series of them have been maintained in the laboratory for over a year, during which the mortalities did not exceed those of normal controls kept for comparison. Grant, and Oscar Anderson, have become very expert practitioners of this form of salamander neurosurgery, and each year since 1962 large series of their "patients" have been released in the experimental stretch and in Jim Creek [83].

The results are not yet as clear-cut and conclusive as we would like, but so far as they go they seem to implicate olfaction as an important factor in homing. For example, we saw earlier that normal animals homed extremely successfully after displacement from the lower portion of the experimental stretch to upper Jim Creek. Out of a total of 692 animals, 171 were captured back at the home site the first year after displacement, and 260 the second year. In a series of similar size (607), animals subjected to precisely the same displacement after section of the olfactory nerves, none at all homed the following year, 5 the second year, and 10 the third year (1965). Of these 15 animals, 13 returned to the home portion of Pepperwood Creek; on dissection, all 15 were found to have regenerated the olfactory nerves, and thus, presumably, to have reacquired the sense of smell. It is tempting to believe that these 15 animals are the forerunners of many more that will yet return from the remote locations to which they have strayed, when regeneration of the olfactory nerves permits them to orient their migrations in the right direction. Captures made during the next few years may or may not confirm this hopeful interpretation. One very real possibility is that anosmia (lack of sense of smell) prevents most animals from surviving the dry summer months, perhaps through interference with detection of moisture and hence in their finding suitable underground niches.

Because of this possibility, we have recently turned to orientation tests that can be initiated and completed within a single spring season, before the approach of summer confronts the anosmic animals with the threat of desiccation. For this testing we are taking advantage of a fact described earlier, namely, that normal animals displaced from one part of the stream to another, and released between two series of land traps, are intercepted primarily in the traps situated in the direction of home.

Here again, however, we encountered an example of the vagaries that may beset research. During the breeding season of 1964 we collected a group of animals from the upper portion of the experimental stretch and, after severing the olfactory nerves, displaced them downstream to Station 46, halfway between the two series of land traps extending transversely to the stream at Stations 43 and 49. During the next few weeks a good percentage of these animals was apprehended in the traps, showing that the series had survived the surgery and was engaging in active movements. Dissection of several showed that there was as yet no trace of olfactory-nerve regeneration. We had expected that their dispersal would be in random directions, confirming the dependence of homing on olfaction, but life is never as simple as this. Like the normal animals subjected to the same displacement the year before, the majority of the recaptures were in the traps leading toward home! On reflection (or should I say rationalization?), however, we decided that this was not necessarily surprising after all. If homing requires olfaction, and the animals were deprived of their bearings by section of the olfactory nerves, would they not then be at the full mercy of the puzzling but definite instinct that causes animals to move upstream on land after leaving the water toward the end of the breeding season?

The test of this hypothesis, of course, was to displace anosmic animals *upstream* to see if later they still moved upstream on land, instead of downstream toward home as would normal animals. Accordingly, in the spring of 1965, we transferred a group of them (413) from the lower portion of the experimental stretch upstream to Station 5, halfway between the two land traps at Stations 1 and 9. For reasons that were not clear (we are getting used to this kind of reason) the total number of captures in the two traps was quite low, only 16 animals: 11 in the upstream trap and 5 in the downstream one. So far as they go these results are quite suggestive, since the corresponding figures for the series of normal animals subjected to the same displacement were 7 and 79. But we dare not base conclusions on so few recaptures, and we shall board the merry-go-round again next season with bigger plans and expectations. In the meantime, even though we have additional data pointing toward olfaction that I shall not take the space to present, we shall withhold any predictions lest the new experiments trip us up with further unexpected findings.

Phenomena of orientation have been much more extensively investigated in frogs and toads than in tailed amphibians, and in these investigations auditory, visual, olfactory, and kinesthetic senses, singly or in combination, have been variously proposed as being instrumental in homing behavior (for examples see references 81, 82, and 84–89). A remarkable situation illustrating the difficulty of the problem is reported by Heusser [90], who found that toads returned to the former sites of their accustomed breeding ponds even after the ponds had been destroyed by road-building operations that altered radically all obvious features that may have served as potential sources of sensory cues to the ponds' locations. More recently Heusser [91 and personal communications] reports that toads with sectioned olfactory nerves still orient toward their breeding sites, and in evaluating his studies with these animals he eliminates one by one all of the senses that might be reasonably proposed as the basis of homing orientation. For some reason I am reminded of my earlier offer to turn the Pepperwood Creek Affair over to the Stanford chaplain.

Before turning to the next topic of the book, however, there are certain arm-chair considerations that obtrude themselves—as they may have upon the mind of the reader—in connection with the possible role of smell in homing. Even if we later prove conclusively that olfaction is the principal sense instrumental in newt navigation, there remain the problems of identifying the sources of the effective odors and of demonstrating how displaced animals can detect them from afar. It is probably safe to assume that the odors do not emanate from the rapidly flowing and hence constantly changing waters of the stream itself. The soil, vegetation, and humus along the streamside are much more probable sources, and one can readily imagine that the varying combinations and quantities of plant species present along the course of a stream might yield different odors for each stream segment. In fact, such differences are sometimes readily detectable even by the insensitive human nostril. Similarly, since the vegetational characteristics of the watersheds of Pepperwood, Jim, and Danfield Creeks are patently different from one another, each stream might have a total odor complex that would differentiate it from its neighbors. Thus we can speculate that a newt displaced from one stream to another might at first be attracted in the general direction of the home stream—perhaps when the wind conditions are favorable—and upon approaching it then begin to channel its movements toward a specific segment of it through more selective discrimination between local odor characteristics. This may seem farfetched, but salmon [92] returning from the ocean to spawn apparently identify the home stream through olfactory discrimination between minute differences in the chemical content of the water.* I readily concede that the imagination must strain itself to grasp how a newt can smell the direction of its home territory after being displaced five miles from Danfield Creek across two mountain ridges into the deep canyon of upper Jim Creek, and if we find that animals

---

* During a recent visit to Seattle I witnessed an almost incredible example of homing accuracy in salmon. This was the return of breeding adults to a small artificial pond that they had left four years earlier after being reared there through fingerling stages by Dr. L. R. Donaldson and his group at the University of Washington. After growing to maturity in the open Pacific they entered Puget Sound and followed the canal leading toward Lake Washington until they relocated the tiny ditch emptying into the canal from their birthplace. All other salmon heading toward Lake Washington and its tributaries show proper contempt for this trivial channel, but its chemical invitation is promptly accepted by migrants who retain memories of the pond imprinted during early youth.

displaced for much greater distances can do the same thing, I too will be strongly inclined to look elsewhere for the explanation of homing.* Any constructive suggestions of just *where* (!) to look will be gratefully received. But please do not ask us to go hunting for tunnels.

THE MEANING OF HOMING

Biologically, of course, the most important point about homing is the simple fact of homing itself, not its sensory physiology or other details. In assessing the significance of homing behavior, one must inquire why association with a particular segment of a particular stream—certainly one of the subtlest manifestations imaginable of the delicate rapport that exists between animals and their environments—is of such compelling importance to newts. It is a fairly safe assumption that the answer is in terms of practical advantages crucial to the welfare and survival of the species. One dividend is the stabilization or equalization of the distribution of individuals within the area occupied by a population, so that competition for food and other environmental necessities, such as suitable terrestrial hiding niches during the dry summer months, will be minimized. A more important benefit, well illustrated in the study area, is protection against what we may call reproductive wastage. Anyone familiar with the smaller California coastal streams knows that many dwindle and disappear during the dry season. The part of Pepperwood Creek referred to as the experimental stretch remains live throughout the year, but immediately downstream where the creek enters a meadow it sinks underground in the summer for a distance of several hundred yards. Earlier in the year this meadow stretch is fully suitable for spawning, but rarely does *rivularis* enter it. Any that were careless enough to choose it for egg-laying would leave few, if any, heirs, since most of the gill-breathing tadpoles hatching from the eggs would not survive the forthcoming drought. Fortunately the species is protected against such errors of judgment by the homing instinct, which ensures that spawning will be confined to waters of proven suitability—proven by the fact that the spawners themselves were born and survived there.

Life-Span and Reproductive Potential

Dealing with as many newts as we have during the conduct of the ranch project, we have inevitably learned about several aspects of their biology that

---

* See footnote, page 131!

we did not set out to investigate. This section will deal with a couple of these, namely, (1) life-span, or longevity, and (2) frequency of breeding. These two features are complementary, since the total reproductive potential of any organism is measurable in terms of the number of times it breeds—together, of course, with the numbers of gametes produced each time—during the course of its life.

The reader will already have gathered, from references to recent captures of animals marked early in the course of the project, that *rivularis* is by no means an ephemeral creature. Just how long individuals of this species may live is not yet known, for the simple reason that we are still recapturing surprisingly high percentages of the groups marked during our first years at the ranch. In 1953, the first year of the project, we marked two series of adult males, one large group numbering 1,835 and a relatively small one of 262. During the breeding season of 1964, eleven years later, we recaptured 28 percent and 30 percent, respectively, of the members of these two series. This, of course, does not include all members of the series surviving in 1964, since not all males enter the water for breeding each year, and a few of those that do undoubtedly escape detection in our patrols. Knowing this, we gave a distinguishing mark to all members caught that year, so that the following year, 1965, we could distinguish them from any new members encountered. Additional captures in 1965 brought the total numbers of recaptures in 1964 and 1965 to 38 percent and 36 percent, respectively, for the two series. At least a few more members of the groups will unquestionably be captured in 1966, which means that about 40 percent of the adults marked in 1953 were still alive eleven years later in 1964, the first year of the three-year census. In a third series, comprising 636 animals first marked in 1955, the recaptures during 1964 and 1965 showed a survival of 41 percent.

Significantly, in all of these series the percentages of recaptures decrease very little from year to year. Detailed data on the recaptures made each year since the series were initiated will be presented later as part of a special publication on life-span in *rivularis,* but I may say here that the annual decrements in recaptures are so small that we fully expect to be encountering some of these old friends in our stream patrols many years hence—if, in fact, the series do not outlast their census takers. Incidentally, the tenacity with which they cling to life may seem even more impressive when it is pointed out that the first two series were originally marked by amputation of an entire hind limb, and the third by a hind limb and one front foot; and that for several years after first marking the three series these appendages were reamputated each year the animals were recaptured during our patrols. If the reader is shocked by this seeming callousness, I hope he will at least concede that although the amputations can hardly have lengthened life-span, neither have they brought the majority of the animals to an unduly early grave.

We can safely conclude, then, that once *rivularis* reaches adulthood it enjoys a rather long period of immunity to the ravages of time and other tormentors, during which it can engage in reproduction and thereby assure perpetuation of the species. My understanding is that most newts, such as those common in Europe, breed each year during their period of maturity, and thus fully utilize their reproductive potential. In *rivularis* this pattern seems definitely to be modified, especially in the female, who in her capacity as egg layer plays a more limiting role in productivity than her male consort.

Our data on the males' frequency of breeding comes from our studies on homing. Rarely are more than 60 percent of the males that have been marked—but not displaced—during a given year, found in the stream again the following year, although in one unusual series the recaptures were almost 80 percent. Thus our conclusion, based on this and other types of evidence, is that a given male will commonly, but definitely not always, breed in immediately successive years.

Females breed much less frequently. Each year since 1960 we have marked all females encountered in our patrols of the experimental stretch, using a distinctive toe clipping for each year. As shown in the tabulation, the pattern of subsequent recaptures has been closely similar in each year-group. The number of females returning to the water the first year following marking is uniformly low in all year-groups, from 0.7 percent to 2.3 percent. The number increases sharply in the second and subsequent years, but the total captures for the oldest series (1960) are still, after five years, far short of the total originally marked. This, together with the fact that the number of new (that is, previously unmarked) females found in the experimental stretch has continued to be about the same each year, indicates that the intervals between successive breedings may vary from one to several years. This explains a phenomenon that

FEMALES MARKED		PERCENTAGE OF FEMALES RECAPTURED				
YEAR	NUMBER	1ST YEAR	2ND YEAR	3RD YEAR	4TH YEAR	5TH YEAR
1960	1,273	.7	14	19	9.2	10.2
1961	836	2.3	13	16.5	10	
1962	1,158	1.0	16	19		
1963	1,295	1.0	18			
1964	1,025	2.3				

had puzzled us earlier, namely, that we always encountered many more males than females in our patrols. An interesting corollary of this is the keen competition among males; it is not unusual to see twenty or more males attempting to mate with a single female.

Since, until recently, all females marked in a given year were marked identically, we were unable to establish the frequency of breeding of individual members of the series. For example, in the series first marked in 1960, the 19 percent captured three years later may well include a few of the 14 percent that had been recaptured the preceding year. But the number of such duplicate captures would always be very small, since not more than 2 to 3 percent of females breed in immediately successive years. Beginning with the 1964 breeding season, the females were marked serially by coded toe clipping, and henceforth our recaptures will permit us to record breeding frequencies of individual animals. This will also be true of large numbers of males marked serially during the past three years.

This difference in breeding frequency between the two sexes, and especially the great variability in the interval between successive breedings of a female, present an unusual picture that to my knowledge is unique among amphibians and perhaps other vertebrates as well.

The low average frequency of breeding for females means that the total production of eggs is considerably less than we might have estimated from the long life-span of the species. In a population that is at equilibrium with its environment, that is, is neither increasing nor decreasing significantly in size, the average lifetime production of a female is only two offspring, one of each sex, that survive to breeding maturity. We must assume that the balance between life-span and frequency of breeding in *rivularis* has been arrived at through processes of natural selection that assure a suitable adjustment between population size and the capacity of the environment to accommodate it. To put it bluntly, since *rivularis* lives so long, presumably it doesn't "need" to breed very often to guarantee maintenance of population size. I can think of one factor that might conceivably select in favor of variability in frequency of female spawning. The eggs of *rivularis,* which are mostly attached to relatively small stones or boulders in the stream bed, are vulnerable to the silting and scouring forces of strong spring floods, and in years when there have been heavy late rains, examination of the streams during the summer often reveals that the crop of surviving larvae is very small. Although I am not quite confident of the logic of the inference, it seems possible that wide variability in the frequency of female spawning might help assure that cataclysmic floods would never destroy the progeny of more than a permissible fraction of the total pool of females in the population.

The Hybridization Experiments

The preceding detour into homing and other topics has carried us rather far afield from the original purpose of the Pepperwood Creek Affair. As I indicated earlier, in its inception the object of the work at the ranch was to throw some light on the genetics and speciation of California newts, not on their behavior. But both studies have been proceeding concurrently, and I can now return to the hybrid planting program, and to the answers it has provided to certain simple but crucial questions that always arise when one attempts to look more closely into the relationships within a genus of organisms. Do or can the member species form viable and fertile hybrids? If so, why do sympatric species (those occupying the same area and thus having breeding access to one another) preserve their separate identities; that is, what are the "isolating mechanisms" that prevent interbreeding? Would species that are *not* sympatric, if it were not for their geographical isolation, prove capable of interbreeding successfully—and if so, what would the ultimate consequences be?

To test these and related questions we have attempted to convert the experimental stretch of Pepperwood Creek into a sort of genetic testing ground, or genetic melting pot [74]. Since 1953 we have produced by artificial hybridization, and introduced into the stream as young tadpoles or newly metamorphosed juveniles, large numbers of three different interspecific combinations. We have also planted larvae of the species that are not native to that part of the State. In other words, we are messing up nature rather badly in Pepperwood Creek.

We knew at the outset that the odds were, if anything, against the probability that the hybrids would be fertile. Sterility is the rule rather than the exception in hybrids of the species and subspecies of European newts, and also in those of the Asiatic newts that have been studied [93–100]. With this glum prospect in mind, we took the following considerations into account in designing the hybrid experiments.

As explained in an earlier chapter, the ancestral *granulosa*-like *Taricha* has evolved along two main lines, one yielding the present-day *granulosa,* and the other differentiating into *rivularis* and the subspecies of *torosa.* On the assumption that the prospects of obtaining fertile hybrids might be increased by closeness of relationship of the parental species, our crosses for the first few years were made only between *rivularis* and the two races of *torosa.* There was also another feature that seemed to favor this choice of hybrid combinations. *Granulosa* is sympatric with the other three forms, while the latter have never been found to occur together in the same immediate vicinities. It was therefore plausible to conjecture that more effective, and possibly more deep-seated, reproductive barriers or isolating mechanisms may have become established between *granulosa* and the other forms than those existing between these three forms themselves. For these reasons, as well as the necessity of keeping the program within workable limits, we concentrated at first on two interspecific hybrid combinations. Using *rivularis* eggs for both crosses, we fertilized them *en masse* with sperm of either *torosa* or *sierrae,* and later released the young hybrids in the experimental stretch.

The longevity figures in the preceding chapter show that once *Taricha* reaches maturity it is slow about dying. Unfortunately for these genetic studies, they are also painfully slow about growing up. The first mature hybrid was not recovered in the experimental stretch until 1959, six years after the first planting of hybrid larvae. (By that time we were beginning to wonder if all our efforts had gone down the drain, and the student who found this first hybrid was insufferable for days.) Since that time the recaptures have steadily increased, and a total of about six hundred adult hybrids have now been recorded, most of which have been marked individually by coded toe clipping. Recaptures of immature hybrids, and the continued planting of new series, assure that a substantial hybrid population will continue to be available almost indefinitely for genetic and other studies.

A full characterization of the *rivularis–torosa* and *rivularis–sierrae* adults would not be appropriate here, but it may be said that they are readily distinguishable from one another and from the native *rivularis* [101]. *Rivularis–torosa* adults are much lighter in dorsal coloration than those of *rivularis,* and in fact are strikingly similar in general appearance to adults of the paternal form, *torosa.* They are immediately distinguishable from them, however, by the pigmentation of the iris (Fig. 55). In *torosa* the iris is profusely pigmented with brightly colored chromatophores; in adult *rivularis* the eye is invariably a dark chocolate brown. The hybrid iris is intermediate in coloration, never as dark as in *rivularis* but definitely less brightly pigmented than in *torosa.* The iris of *rivularis–sierrae* hybrids is of the same intermediate character, in keeping with the fact that *sierrae,* like *torosa,* has a brightly colored eye, but otherwise the hybrids of this combination have a strong superficial resemblance to adults of the maternal species, *rivularis.* On closer examination, however, one finds that whereas in *rivularis* there is heavy encroachment of the dark dorsal pigmentation onto the ventral surfaces of the limbs, and usually a black band extending downward over the lips of the vent, these characteristics are lacking in the *rivularis–sierrae* hybrids.

I think the reader may be interested at this point in a parenthetical reference to a detail of the hybrid recaptures bearing on our homing studies. Since our

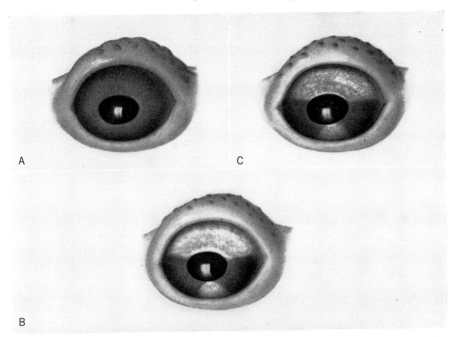

FIGURE 55. *The iris of* rivularis (A) *is dark brown (essentially black), while that of* torosa (C) *is brightly colored by densely packed silvery and yellow pigment cells. In hybrids of the two species (B) these cells are present in much smaller numbers, imparting an intermediate coloration to the iris that (among other features) immediately distinguishes the hybrids from the parental species.*

marking experiments were all performed with adult animals they could not reveal whether identification with a given segment of stream is "imprinted" at the time of first entry as mature adults or much earlier, either during larval life or at the time the newts leave the water as newly metamorphosed juveniles and make their first reconnaisance of the streamside environment. When planting the hybrid larvae, we released the *rivularis–torosa* tadpoles in roughly the upper third of the experimental stretch, and those of *rivularis–sierrae* in approximately the lower third. Of the large numbers of adult hybrids that have since been recaptured all except a very few have been found in the stream sections in which they had been planted. This suggests strongly that association with specific breeding sites is fixed in early life. If imprinting occurred several years later, at the time of the first return to the stream for breeding, it seems unlikely that the stream segments chosen would correspond as closely as they do to the places where the animals lived during infancy.

TARICHA PASSES ANOTHER TEST

The hybrids are fully as large and seem to be fully as vigorous as the parental species. But as shown by many examples, including the classical one of the mule, size and vigor are not necessarily an index of fertility, and our initial tests of the hybrid gametes were conducted with almost as much reluctance as anticipation. However, the first trials, made by artificial fertilizations, soon showed that in this as in other respects *Taricha* can do no wrong. The hybrids, both males and females, were definitely not in the mule category.

In assessing the genetic and evolutionary implications of hybridization, one needs to know not only whether a species-hybrid is fertile, but also whether it is fully or only incompletely so. For testing this question, artificial fertilization is not a very satisfactory method, partly because of environmental hazards to the gametes inherent in the procedure itself [101]. The eggs and sperm may be adversely affected and thus cause failures or abnormalities of development that are quite unrelated to any genetic shortcomings of the gametes. Our conviction that variability in the percentages of successful development in our artificial tests was attributable to this cause was later confirmed by natural matings of hybrid adults. For these tests males and females were confined together in large spring-fed tanks at the field laboratory, or in wire enclosures in the stream itself [102]. If it were not for certain identifying hereditary characteristics of the offspring of the hybrids, it would not always be possible to know their paternity, since one cannot be certain that hybrid females have not already been inseminated before capture. But the identifying characteristics are definite and for our present purposes it is sufficient to say that during the past few years these matings have yielded large numbers of eggs whose fertility and viability have been checked by careful observation of their development.

In some series the hybrid females were mated with hybrid males, and in others with males of native *rivularis*. To cover all possibilities, the other back-cross was also tested: *rivularis* females were paired with hybrid males. Large samples of the resulting second-generation embryos have been brought back to Stanford at the end of the spring seasons for observation and rearing in the laboratory. The survival in a typical group of series is shown in the table, together with the results with normal *rivularis* eggs reared for comparison. The figures show that the percentages of fertilization and development to the hatching stage are uniformly very high. It is doubtful that the minor differences among the hybrid series are significant, and it is probably fortuitous that the success of the *rivularis* control series is slightly lower than that of the second-

CROSSES	PERCENT OF EGGS DEVELOPING NORMALLY TO HATCHING	PERCENT OF LARVAE DEVELOPING NORMALLY FROM HATCHING THROUGH METAMORPHOSIS
rivularis–torosa ♀ × *rivularis* ♂	92	89
rivularis–torosa ♀ × *rivularis–torosa* ♂	96	92
rivularis–sierrae ♀ × *rivularis* ♂	97	84
rivularis–sierrae ♀ × *rivularis–sierrae* ♂	94	78
rivularis ♀ × *rivularis–torosa* ♂	91	96.5
normal *rivularis*	90	97

generation combinations. Whether from handling, fungus infections, or unknown causes, there is almost always some mortality in any culture of amphibian eggs, and its incidence varies appreciably and unpredictably even among apparently identical samples of material.

Survival during the subsequent larval period, and through the crucial and difficult period of metamorphosis, is also high in all of the second-generation series. It is true that there were a few more mortalities in the offspring of *rivularis–sierrae* females than among those of *rivularis–torosa* females, and the possibility cannot be discounted that this reflects a genetic inferiority of the former stocks. However, the deterioration, or "hybrid breakdown," cannot be characterized as great, since a survival of approximately eighty percent beyond the most vulnerable period in the life-history is, after all, evidence that the second-generation hybrids still retain considerable vigor and viability.

I have explained why *granulosa* was not included in our hybridization program at the time of its inception. This omission was later corrected, however, following the accidental discovery that hybrids of *granulosa* and the other species might well be fertile in spite of our theorizing to the contrary. In 1958 a male was found in the experimental stretch whose coloration and other characteristics immediately suggested that it was a *rivularis–granulosa* hybrid. It proved to be fertile when its sperm was used for an artificial back-cross to *rivularis*, and the pigmentary features of the young offspring seemed to support fully our identification of the hybrid.

I am sure that the incidence of hybridization between *rivularis* and *granulosa* is very low, since this and a more recently captured specimen are the only natural hybrids that have been encountered among the literally scores of thousands of *rivularis* and *granulosa* adults that we have examined in Pepperwood and other creeks during intensive collection and study over many years. Each breeding season we observe isolated instances of interspecific amplexus, between *granulosa* and *rivularis* adults, but I am convinced that these reflect primarily the highly aggressive and sometimes promiscuous sexual proclivities of male newts and that the matings almost never culminate in insemination.

However, the knowledge that males of this combination are fertile led us immediately to include artificially produced *rivularis–granulosa* hybrids in our planting program, and during the 1965 breeding season several of the resulting adults were found in the experimental stretch. Although we attempted no controlled matings with these hybrids, a few of the females were isolated in separate containers and subsequently spawned fertilized eggs that developed with almost no failures through metamorphosis. Pigmentary features of the larvae showed that in some cases the hybrid mothers had mated with *rivularis* males, and in others with *granulosa* males. Controlled matings, and more extensive tests of viability of the offspring comparable to those reported for the *rivularis–torosa* and *rivularis–sierrae* hybrids, will be made eventually; in the meantime it seems safe to predict that the results will be closely similar.

A DIFFICULT COMPROMISE

I mentioned earlier that one of the features distinguishing *granulosa* from the other species of *Taricha* was the small size of its eggs and the fact that they are deposited singly instead of in clusters [52]. As we had expected, we found that the eggs laid by the *rivularis–granulosa* hybrid females were intermediate in size between the tiny ones of *granulosa* and the massive ones of *rivularis*. But we were at a loss in predicting how the hybrids would compromise between the *granulosa* habit of laying single eggs and the *rivularis* practice of laying clusters of them. Apparently the hybrids themselves recognized the awkwardness of the dilemma and avoided it by making no decisive choice. Each hybrid female deposited most of its eggs singly, and others in pairs or groups of three to five. This intermediacy in egg size and the manner of their deposition is also reflected in the structure of the vent, or cloaca, through which the female emits the eggs in spawning. In *granulosa* the aperture is small, at the apex of a conical or crater-shaped elevation, while in *rivularis* it is a larger, more elongate slit situated in a depression between prominent cloacal lips. In the hybrid females the structure of the cloaca is roughly a compromise between the structures of the parental species (Fig. 56).

HYBRIDIZATION AND EVOLUTION

Why is the rather remarkable success of hybridization in *Taricha* of interest for problems of evolution and systematics? One main reason is that hybridiza-

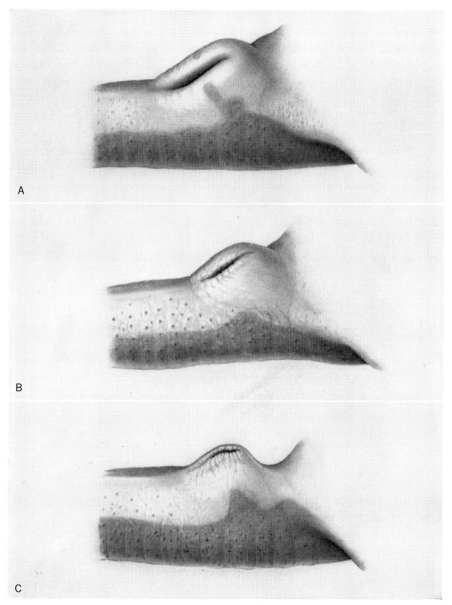

FIGURE 56. *Cloacal (vent) regions of a female* rivularis *(A),* granulosa *(C), and* rivularis-granulosa *hybrid (B). Correlated with the differences in conformation of the vents are differences in egg laying:* rivularis *lays eggs in clusters;* granulosa *deposits them singly; and* rivularis-granulosa *hybrids compromise by laying them singly or in small aggregates (of two to five eggs).*

tion can conceivably play a role in further speciation, since it erects a bridge by which genes can pass from one species to another and thus establish new combinations of hereditary characters. If two species that are ordinarily reproductively isolated chance to interbreed, and the hybrid offspring later mate successfully with one of the parental species, that parental line receives an infusion of genes from the other species that may ultimately result in the emergence of new stocks. This phenomenon, called introgressive hybridization, has apparently played a significant role in the evolution of higher plants [103]. Although there are a few instances where it is believed to have operated in animal speciation as well, as in certain birds, frogs, and fishes, the prevailing opinion concerning its importance in animal evolution is probably that expressed recently by Ernst Mayr [104]. He points out that these examples are, after all, relatively rare, and that the random assemblages of genes produced in this way will usually be imperfectly balanced, or will not be reproductively isolated long enough to establish themselves permanently as distinct and self-perpetuating entities.

I have been aware of these considerations since the beginning of our hybrid planting program, and of the practical difficulty of establishing hybrid populations large enough to have any major impact on the native parental populations. The facts remain, however, that the species-hybrids established in our study have proved to be fertile, do backcross freely and effectively with native *rivularis,* and produce offspring that appear to be vigorous and viable. One can at least say that the prime requisites for infiltration and possible modification of the native gene pool have been met. Whether the potentialities of the situation will actually be realized to a significant extent depends partly on whether the second-generation offspring prove to be as "successful" in nature as they are in our laboratory. Because of the slow pace at which generations of newts succeed one another, the answers to this will undoubtedly accumulate very slowly. In the meantime, the backcross populations arising from voluntary matings in natural environments are being augmented by release of series obtained from controlled matings and artificial fertilizations.

Whatever the eventual outcome of the hybrid planting program, the fertility of the first-generation hybrids has already demonstrated that the various species of *Taricha* have not yet differentiated to the point at which impregnable genetic barriers exist between them; gene exchange through introgressive hybridization is still open as one of the potential avenues for further evolutionary elaboration in the genus. If in the dim, distant future species which now exist only in isolation come together, perhaps hybridization between them will afford the opportunity for a new period of evolutionary flowering. I don't expect, however, that this will happen in time for inclusion of the results in this book, as long and drawn out as the steps leading finally to its publication now seem to loom.

Nature of the Reproductive Barriers

Since there are no major genetic barriers isolating the species of *Taricha*, what *are* the mechanisms that enable them to preserve their integrity as distinct forms? When species occupy different geographical areas there is, of course, no opportunity to interbreed even if they were prone to do so. But this does not explain why *granulosa* remains genetically distinct from the other three species in regions where it is sympatric with them.

I mentioned that we sometimes observe amplexus (clasping of the female by the male) between *rivularis* and *granulosa,* and the finding of two natural hybrids of these species shows that at least occasionally these matings will result in the production of offspring. But the attractions of interspecific mating cannot be great, since its frequency is so low in comparison with the numbers of opportunities for it. The strong preference for mates of the same species has also been demonstrated by tethering females of *rivularis* and *granulosa* side-by-side in the stream. Only rarely will *rivularis* males drawn from downstream by the female scent pay more than passing attention to the *granulosa* female; almost without exception they gather in an importunate cluster around the lady of their own species.

William Davis, a graduate student working at the ranch, has made a comparative study of courtship behavior in the species of *Taricha,* and finds that the nature of the ritual is closely similar in all forms [105]. The male grasps the female firmly from above and rubs his vent across her sacral region by brisk lateral movements of his tail and body. He later dismounts and deposits a white packet of sperm (spermatophore), attaching it by its gelatinous stalk to a pebble on the stream bed or aquarium floor. The female moves after him, apparently guided by the posture he assumes in relation to the location of the spermatophore, which, as she passes over it, adheres to—and later enters—her vent (Fig. 57). The male then often mounts the female again for a second period of amplexus. The whole courtship sequence is rather elaborate, and usually quite precise.

Although Davis found a few minor differences in the mating patterns of the species and subspecies of *Taricha,* they do not seem great enough to serve as barriers to effective interspecific breeding. We cannot be sure, of course, that differences which appear insignificant to the human observer, or are so subtle as

FIGURE 57. *After the male (left) dismounts from the female and deposits a spermatophore he assumes the curved posture shown here. The female responds by moving along his side until her vent is in position to pick up the spermatophore, which is concealed beneath her body in this photograph. Photograph by William Davis, from Davis and Twitty* [105].

to escape detection by him, may not block courtship at one point or another during mating. At the moment, however, we favor the possibility that the sex attractants released by the females are important in reproductive isolation, as they are thought to be in European newts. The problem requires more study, and I shall refer only briefly to evidence pointing toward implication of the female secretions.

The evidence comes from interspecific mating tests made both in the presence and in the absence of conspecific females or of their secretions. In tests with *rivularis* and *granulosa*, the males made virtually no attempt to clasp females of the other species unless females of their own species, or water in which they had been stored, were introduced into the aquarium. Even then the induced amplexus was brief, suggesting perhaps that if species–specific sex attractants are deeply involved in courtship, they were not present in sufficient concentration to effect completion of interspecific mating. Incidentally, blinded *rivularis* males, recaptured in the stream following removal of the eyes in previous seasons, showed the same ability as normal males to distinguish conspecific from heterospecific females.

But what of allopatric species (those occupying different regions)? Granted that they normally have no opportunity to interbreed, would they do so if brought together? There is some indication that reproductive barriers (species–specific sex attractants?) are somewhat less developed between allopatric forms. For example, in the early tests with tethered females it was noted that although *rivularis* males were seldom attracted to *granulosa* females, they sometimes showed marked interest in those of the two subspecies of *torosa,* especially those of *sierrae* [79]. This was also observed, in less pronounced form, in aquarium tests. Here again, however, the incidence and duration of interspecific amplexus was greater in the presence of conspecific females or of their secretions.

A serious limitation to experimentation with allopatric forms is the difficulty of obtaining test material in prime mating condition when one species has to be transported for considerable distances. Successful mating in captivity is uncertain, even in tests with males and females of the same species, unless both have been freshly collected from the stream. For this reason we believe the most reliable and significant observations will be those made with the *torosa* and *sierrae* adults that we hope will become available in the study area as a result of our planting program. Only a few adults of these forms have been captured following the release of larvae some years ago. It may be relevant, however, to mention a *torosa* female found in a small tributary of the experimental stream during the 1962 breeding season [105]. A few days after isolation in a small aquarium she deposited clusters of fertilized eggs that later proved to be of *rivularis* paternity. This was clear from paternal effects with which we are familiar from artificial fertilizations of *torosa* eggs by *rivularis* sperm, namely, the modification of the larval pigment pattern and reduction or absence of the balancer in hybrids of these species. We do not know, of course, whether the mating had been "facilitated" by the presence of *rivularis* females.

This observation suggests that *torosa* and *rivularis,* which do not encounter one another in nature, may not have developed effective intrinsic barriers to hybridization. We doubt that such barriers are completely lacking, but we believe that the answer to the question may have to await not merely more extensive aquarium tests with transported adults, but the results of additional interspecific encounters under the natural conditions that we are trying to utilize in our planting program. The reader has already seen that any intrinsic barriers isolating the parental species disappear completely with hybridization: the mature species–hybrids mate freely and successfully with the parental species.

During the past two years we have resumed the planting of normal *torosa* larvae in the experimental stretch in an attempt to build up a population of this species large enough for more extensive tests of their willingness and ability to interbreed with *rivularis*. Unlike more accommodating organisms, such as fruit flies and mice, the slow-growing *torosa* is in no hurry to mature and provide us with early answers to this question. But we are in no great haste, and the last thing we wish is the solution of all the questions raised by the Pepperwood Creek Affair, compelling us to fold up our field station and slink back to our basement laboratories at home.

Professor Carl Hubbs, a noted ichthyologist and authority on natural hybridization, commented recently in a personal communication that the role played by genetic barriers (if, indeed, these have a role) in isolating the species of *Taricha* is paralleled nicely in certain groups of fishes. When species are brought together in an area where usually only one lives, hybridization will often follow even though the same pair of species "behave themselves" in a region where they are naturally sympatric. As Dr. Hubbs points out, the factors that block hybridization in nature must indeed be varied and delicate.

Some Elementary Genetics

What have we learned about the genetics of the species of *Taricha* by our hybridization experiments? Needless to say, probably neither we nor any one else will ever know as much about hereditary transmission in newts as is already known about many organisms with shorter generation times, but some information is better than none, and we have not come away empty-handed. I shall give a very curtailed presentation of the genetic data, since a comprehensive account of the results in all of the various interspecific combinations might be more confusing than enlightening.

Among the first characters attracting my attention to *Taricha* were the striking species differences in the arrangements of the larval melanophores. Because of this and because of the desire to "close the circle" by learning something about the genetics of the cells whose development I had investigated intensively, I had long been curious about how the pigment patterns would be affected by hybridization and especially how they would sort out in the second hybrid generation. The contrasting patterns of young *torosa* and *rivularis* larvae, described and illustrated earlier, are shown again in Figure 58, A, B. In *torosa* almost all of the melanophores are compacted into a pair of dorsal bands, whereas in *rivularis* they are widely and uniformly dispersed over the flanks. When *rivularis* eggs are fertilized by *torosa* sperm, the resulting arrangement of the melanophores shows features of both parental patterns, although the well-defined dorsal band imparts a closer resemblance to the *torosa* pattern (Fig. 58, C). If one's patience holds out for about five or six years while these hybrids grow to maturity, he can then learn something about the numbers of genes responsible for the striking differences in *rivularis* and *torosa* pigment patterns. Taking sperm from a hybrid male, for example, we can fertilize eggs

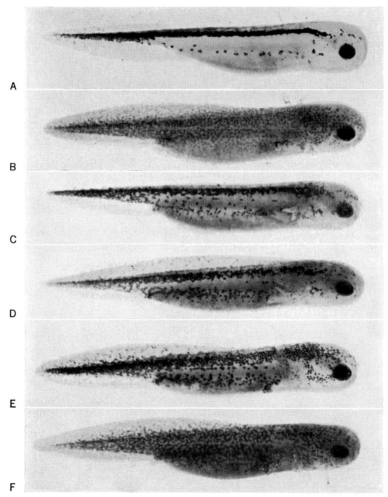

FIGURE 58. A *and* B: *Young larvae of* torosa *and* rivularis, *respectively.* C: Rivularis ♀ × torosa ♂ *hybrid.* D, E, *and* F: *offspring of* rivularis ♀ × rivularis-torosa ♂ *hybrid, illustrating segregation of pigment patterns closely similar to those of the hybrid* (D) *and* rivularis (F) *parents, and a pattern intermediate to these two* (E).

of a *rivularis* female and see what types and ratios of pigment patterns emerge among the offspring.

In several series of this kind we found that most of the patterns could be classified into three basic categories, examples of which are shown in Figure 58, D, E, F. One of these is essentially indistinguishable from the maternal *rivularis* pattern, a second similarly duplicates the pattern of the *rivularis–torosa* father, and the third is approximately intermediate to these two. Of 820 young larvae scored, 339 and 206, respectively, fell into the first two groups, and 275 into the third.

There is some variation in pattern among the larvae in each category, but the scoring standards were reasonably strict, and in few cases did the patterns assigned to given categories deviate very substantially from those shown in the photographs. Although I shall not, on the basis of these data, venture specific estimates of how many genes or gene-blocks are responsible for the differences in the *torosa* and *rivularis* patterns, it seems obvious that the number must be quite limited; otherwise the two parental pigment patterns, *rivularis* and hybrid-type, could hardly have segregated in such large ratios among the backcross offspring. Scoring of other characters in which *torosa* and *rivularis* differ, such as the size or presence of the balancer, the length of the dorsal fin, and the coloration of skin and eye after metamorphosis, indicate that these differences have also arisen through mutations affecting relatively small numbers of genes [101]. As was probably to be expected, these various features appear to segregate independently of one another, showing that they have arisen independently by mutation of genes located on different chromosomes. For example, a second-generation larva with a hybrid-type pigment pattern may either possess or lack a balancer, and its dorsal fin may or may not be reduced. Similarly, larvae with a *rivularis*-type pigment pattern are no more prone to develop at metamorphosis the dark-colored iris and intense blackening of the dorsal body skin characteristic of normal *rivularis* than are those with a banded, hybrid-type pigment pattern.

In the F_2 generation, obtained when both parents are hybrids instead of only one as in the backcross series, the spectrum of larval pigment patterns and other characters segregating among the offspring is a broader one, ranging all the way between the extremes represented by the two parent species. Thus it becomes possible to recover both the strikingly banded pattern of *torosa* and the diffuse arrangement of melanophores characteristic of *rivularis*. These two extremes, as well as intermediate types, are illustrated by the larvae in Figure 59, selected from the offspring of a *rivularis-torosa* female whose eggs were fertilized artificially by sperm from a hybrid male. However, for unknown

FIGURE 59. *Offspring of a* rivularis-torosa ♀ *hybrid inseminated by a* rivularis-torosa ♂ *hybrid. These four offspring were selected to illustrate the spectrum of pigment patterns ranging from* torosa-*type* (A) *through intermediate types* (B *and* C) *to one* (D) *that approaches the* rivularis-*type pattern.*

reasons that I have speculated about elsewhere [101], the assortment of patterns is heavily weighted on the *torosa* side of the spectrum, and very few strictly *rivularis*-type patterns ever emerge in the F_2 generations of this hybrid combination.

As the Pepperwood experiments continue we expect to learn more from our expanding and diversifying hybrid populations about the genetics and probable evolutionary relationships of the species of *Taricha*. An important added dividend, we believe, will be the use of our hybrid material for other purposes. I mentioned earlier the comparisons by Michael Coates of the *Taricha* serum proteins, and the use of hybrid serum greatly enriches the opportunities for analytical studies of this kind. I am confident also that the unique hybrid stocks will lend themselves for chemical and cytological studies in developmental genetics, and workers elsewhere have already begun to use them to investigate inheritance of enzyme patterns and the onset of gene action during early development.

Our principal concern is that opportunities of this nature may seduce us back into the laboratory, but since others are much better equipped for exploiting these possibilities of our material, I suspect we shall continue to sink our roots ever deeper in the congenial soil of Sonoma County.

Redemption or Downfall?

I have been asked several times what prompted me to shift my research from the embryology of newts to their ecology, speciation, and behavior. The presumption seems to be that no one would make such a move without profound motives or careful calculation. Did I perhaps feel that I had run my course as an embryologist, or that the subject was becoming too chemical for my tastes and aptitudes anyway? Or had I decided that progress in embryology was approaching something of a temporary stalemate and that easier and richer dividends were to be found in less fashionable and hence less crowded fields? Or did I think the time was approaching when experimental biologists could profitably return to Mother Nature's vast outdoor laboratory, from which all perspective and inspiration must periodically be renewed if biology is to remain biology instead of becoming a fleshless abstraction?

As their tones reveal, some of the inquiries have come from those who approved of my switch, and others from those who could only view it as defection and downfall. In some cases the question has been put with apparent reluctance and even embarrassment, as if commiserating with a musician who had turned from Bach to boogie-woogie or with a virtuous woman who was leaning toward sin.

Almost no one has seemed inclined to accept the true and simple reason for my shift (whether it be in the direction of downfall or of redemption), namely, that it just happened that way. I believe by now the book should have made it abundantly clear that once we released some artificially produced newt hybrids in nature for the somewhat casual purpose of rearing them to maturity for tests of their fertility, I was hooked. Questions immediately arose concerning such things as home range and homing behavior, and before I knew it I was inextricably—but not unwillingly—engaged in studies that gradually preempted all the time and energy previously devoted to embryology. I will admit that after years of grafting and culturing almost endless thousands of tiny pieces of tissue these maneuvers may have begun to lose some of their novelty, and it was refreshing to be confronted—especially in a setting so much to my liking—with problems new to my experience and training. But I had not tired of embryology, nor was there any question of value judgments concerning the relative merits or ore-content of embryology and "natural history."

Discriminatory judgments about the importance of different fields or levels of biology are in my opinion intellectually naive. Of course, the practice of making them is not new. I would naturally like to think that in the "good old days" biologists were more tolerant of one another's tastes and specialties, and that it could not have happened then that the molecular biologist would condemn the crudities of other approaches or that the ecologist would scoff at the microbial geneticist for his preoccupation with "nothing larger than macromolecules." But this nostalgia is unfortunately unwarranted, as I can well remember from the mutual disdain with which we budding embryologists, protozoologists, and endocrinologists professed to regard all except our own provinces, forty years ago at Osborn Laboratory.

I wouldn't give a nickel for a biologist who isn't sufficiently enthusiastic about his specialty to rate it a cut better than most others, but refusal to grant the same luxury of opinion to laborers in other fields, or open expression of contempt for their endeavors, is now as always one of the least attractive and most unscientific traits a scientist can have. Who is to say, except in arrogance, which fields and which facets are transcendent in inherent importance and interest? Fortunately for the advancement of knowledge, there are built-in sources of protection against such arbitrary verdicts. Heredity and environment have seen to it that some biologists—stubborn fellows!—gravitate inevitably towards birds, bees, or mosses, while others, equally benighted, turn to axones, genes, or hormones. (Some of them are even perverse enough to feel that it is unimportant whether their contributions bear the labels of botany or plant biology, of embryology or developmental biology, or of biochemistry or molecular biology.) In this way biology has managed to keep some semblance of balance, and hopefully always will.

Not long ago I had an inquiry from a college dean asking me to nominate a department head "who will introduce at least a modicum of the new molecular in biology" into the institution's curriculum. When harrassed deans of the future make frantic pleas for teachers who will introduce a trace of the new populational, or maybe even restore ("quick, for Heaven's sake") a measure of the old organismic—we can but hope that they too will find someone to give them sympathy and support. Like the confident architects and prophets of science today, they will often be sore confused, and know not what they do.

To any young—or even aging—laboratory biologist who has a little spare time and feels that molecules and cells are moving in on him too menacingly, I suggest he scan his circle of acquaintances for a landowner who might loan him a rural niche where the flora or fauna can be tinkered with. If he is strong of character, and sufficiently loyal to his training, he can refresh himself afield and still maintain his foothold in the laboratory. But he had best beware, for if he lacks resolve, or is gifted in the rationalization of values—well, you have seen what can happen to him.

Collateral Reading

Most of the literature citations in the text are to original scientific articles, in which interested readers can find more detailed documentation of the subject matter of the book. There are, however, references to a few publications of a more comprehensive nature, and it may be helpful if these, together with a limited number of other books of similar scope, are described here for those who may wish to explore in breadth any of the main topics dealt with in *Of Scientists and Salamanders*.

Bonner's *Morphogenesis: An essay on development* [106] is a very readable account of principles and experiments in the field of development. At a considerably more technical level, *Analysis of Development* [107], edited by Willier, Weiss, and Hamburger, offers authoritative chapters on a wide range of developmental topics. Spemann's *Embryonic Development and Induction* [2] is an invaluable historical account of the earlier studies on the organizer and of the experiments leading to its discovery; and Saxen and Toivonen's *Primary Embryonic Induction* [38] is an exhaustive review of more recent investigations of the organizer. Willier and Oppenheimer, in *Foundations of Experimental Embryology* [108], bring together eleven original papers published between 1888 and 1939 by pioneering investigators including four, Harrison, Spemann, Child, and Holtfreter, who play prominent parts in the present book.

In the field of animal orientation, perhaps the most comprehensive and least technical survey is Carty's *Animal Navigation: How Animals Find Their Way About* [109]. Matthew's *Bird Navigation* [110], Schmidt-Koenig's *Current Problems in Bird Orientation* [111], and Griffin's *Bird Migration* [112] give thorough treatments of avian homing behavior. *Readings in Animal Behavior* [113], edited by McGill, includes several original articles dealing with orientation in bats, bees, porpoises, and other animals. Although it does not deal with phenomena of orientation, one of the most delightful books in all of biology is *King Solomon's Ring* [114], in which the great student of animal behavior, Konrad Lorenz, presents a penetrating and affectionate account of his lifetime association with a variety of captive animals, including a series of unusual pets who enlivened and sometimes dominated his household.

Literature Cited

[1] Child, C. M. 1924. *Physiological Foundations of Behavior*. Henry Holt, New York. 330 p.

[2] Spemann, Hans. 1938. *Embryonic Development and Induction*. Yale University Press, New Haven. 401 p.

[3] Twitty, V. C. 1955. Organogenesis: the eye. P. 402–414 in *Analysis of Development* [107].

[4] Harrison, R. G. 1907. Experiments in transplanting limbs and their bearing on the problems of development of nerves. *J. Exp. Zool.*, **4**: 239–281.

[5] Harrison, R. G. 1910. The outgrowth of the nerve fiber as a mode of protoplasmic movement. *J. Exp. Zool.*, **9**: 787–846.

[6] Oppenheimer, J. 1965. Ross Granville Harrison. In *Geschichte der Mikroskopie* (Leben und Werk grosser Forscher). Band II: Medizin, p. 117–126. Frankfurt.

[7] Harrison, R. G. 1918. Experiments on the development of the fore limb of *Amblystoma*, a self-differentiating equipotential system. *J. Exp. Zool.*, **25**: 413–461.

[8] Harrison, R. G. 1921. On relations of symmetry in transplanted limbs. *J. Exp. Zool.*, **32**: 1–136.

[9] Harrison, R. G. 1925. The effect of reversing the medio-lateral or transverse axis of the forelimb bud in the salamander embryo (*Amblystoma punctatum* Linn.). *Arch. EntwMech. Org.*, **106**: 469–502.

[10] Weiss, Paul. 1939. *Principles of Development*. Henry Holt, New York. 601 p.

[11] Twitty, V. C. 1928. Experimental studies on the ciliary action of amphibian embryos. *J. Exp. Zool.*, **50**: 319–344.

[12] Jacobson, A. G. 1958. The roles of neural and non-neural tissues in lens induction. *J. Exp. Zool.*, **139**: 525–557.

[13] Twitty, V. C., and D. Bodenstein. 1941. Experiments on the determination problem. I. The roles of ectoderm and neural crest in the development of the dorsal fin in Amphibia. II. Changes in ciliary polarity associated with the induction of fin epidermis. *J. Exp. Zool.*, **86**: 343–380.

[14] Abercrombie, M. 1961. Ross Granville Harrison. *Biographical Memoirs of Fellows of the Royal Society,* 7: 111–126.

[15] Harrison, R. G. 1924. Some unexpected results of the heteroplastic transplantation of limbs. *Proc. Nat. Acad. Sci.,* 10:69–74.

[16] Harrison, R. G. 1933. Heteroplastic grafting in embryology. *The Harvey Lectures,* 1933–34, Ser. 29, p. 116–157.

[17] Twitty, V. C., and J. L. Schwind. 1931. The growth of eyes and limbs transplanted heteroplastically between two species of *Amblystoma. J. Exp. Zool.,* 59: 61–86.

[18] Twitty, V. C., and H. A. Elliott. 1934. The relative growth of the amphibian eye, studied by means of transplantation. *J. Exp. Zool.,* 68: 247–291.

[19] Copenhaver, W. M. 1939. Some observations on the growth and function of heteroplastic heart grafts. *J. Exp. Zool.,* 82: 239–271.

[20] Harrison, R. G. 1929. Correlation in the development and growth of the eye studied by means of heteroplastic transplantation. *Arch. EntwMech. Org.,* 120: 1–55.

[21] Twitty, V. C. 1932. Influence of the eye on the growth of its associated structures, studied by means of heteroplastic transplantation. *J. Exp. Zool.,* 61: 333–374.

[22] Heath, H. D. 1953. Regeneration and growth of chimaeric amphibian limbs. *J. Exp. Zool.,* 122: 339–366.

[23] Church, G. 1956. The growth and morphology of *Amblystoma* chimeras. *J. Morph.,* 98: 405–428.

[24] Twitty, V. C. 1930. Regulation in the growth of transplanted eyes. *J. Exp. Zool.,* 55: 43–52.

[25] Heath, H. D. 1957. Growth regulation in *Amblystoma* eyes transplanted between larvae of different ages. *J. Exp. Zool.,* 135: 425–444.

[26] Twitty, V. C. 1940. Size-controlling factors. *Growth Supplement* [1940]: 109–120.

[27] Twitty, V. C. and L. E. DeLanney. 1939. Size regulation and regeneration in salamander larvae under complete starvation. *J. Exp. Zool.,* 81: 399–414.

[28] Twitty, V. C., and W. J. van Wagtendonk. 1940. A suggested mechanism for the regulation of proportionate growth, supported by quantitative data on the blood nutrients. *Growth,* 4: 349–360.

[29] Spemann, H., and Hilde Mangold. 1924. Ueber Induktion von Embryonalanlagen durch Implantation artfremder Organisatoren. *Arch. f. mikr. Anat. u. EntwMech.,* 100: 599–638. English translation in *Foundations of Experimental Embryology* [108].

[30] Hamburger, V. 1960. *A Manual of Experimental Embryology.* University of Chicago Press, Chicago. 220 p.

[31] Holtfreter, J., and Hamburger, V. 1955. Embryogenesis: Progressive differentiation. Amphibians. P. 230–296 in *Analysis of Development* [107].

[32] Holtfreter, J. 1933. Die totale Exogastrulation, eine Selbstablösung des Ektoderms von Entomesoderm. *Arch. EntwMech. Org.,* 129: 669–793.

[33] Mangold, O. 1931. Versuche zur Analyse der Entwicklung des Haftfadens bei Urodelen; ein Beispiel für die Induktion artfremder Organe. *Naturwissenschaften,* 19: 905–911.

[34] Holtfreter, J. 1933. Nachweis der Induktionsfähigkeit abgetöteter Keimteile. *Arch. EntwMech. Org.,* **128:** 584–633.

[35] Holtfreter, J. 1934. Ueber die Verbreitung induzierender Substanzen und ihre Leistungen im *Triton*-Keim. *Arch. EntwMech. Org.,* **132:** 307–383.

[36] Barth, L. G. 1941. Neural differentiation without organizer. *J. Exp. Zool.,* **87:** 371–383.

[37] Holtfreter, J. 1944. Neural differentiation of gastrula ectoderm. *J. Exp. Zool.,* **95:** 307–340.

[38] Saxen, L., and S. Toivonen. 1961. *Primary Embryonic Induction.* Prentice-Hall, Englewood Cliffs, N.J., 271 p.

[39] Twitty, V. C., and M. C. Niu. 1954. The motivation of cell migration, studied by isolation of embryonic pigment cells singly and in small groups *in vitro. J. Exp. Zool.,* **125:** 541–574.

[40] Niu, M. C., and V. C. Twitty. 1953. The differentiation of gastrula ectoderm in medium conditioned by axial mesoderm. *Proc. Nat. Acad. Sci.,* **39:** 985–989.

[41] Barth, L. G., and L. J. Barth. 1959. Differentiation of cells of the *Rana pipiens* gastrula in unconditioned medium. *J. Embryol. Exp. Morph.,* **7:** 210–222.

[42] Holtfreter, J. 1951. Some aspects of embryonic induction. *Growth* (suppl.), **10:** 117–152.

[43] Twitty, V. C. 1942. The role of genetic differentials in the embryonic development of Amphibia. *Biological Symposia,* **6:** 291–310.

[44] Whitaker, D. M. 1940. Physical factors of growth. *Growth Supplement* [1940] 75–90.

[45] Child, C. M. 1941. *Patterns and Problems of Development.* University of Chicago Press, Chicago. 811 p.

[46] Twitty, V. C. 1937. Experiments on the phenomenon of paralysis produced by a toxin occurring in *Triturus* embryos. *J. Exp. Zool.,* **76:** 67–104.

[47] Mosher, H. S., F. A. Fuhrman, H. D. Buchwald, and H. G. Fischer. 1964. Tarichatoxin-Tetrodotoxin: A potent neurotoxin. *Science,* **144:** 1100–1110.

[48] Storer, T. I. 1925. A synopsis of the Amphibia of California. *Univ. Calif. Publ. Zool.,* **27:** 1–342.

[49] Noble, G. K. 1931. *Biology of the Amphibia.* McGraw-Hill, New York. 577 p. (Reprinted in 1954 by Dover Publications, New York.)

[50] Twitty, V. C. 1964. *Taricha rivularis,* red-bellied newt. P. 9.1–9.2 in W. J. Riemer, ed., *Catalog of American Amphibians and Reptiles.* American Society of Ichthyologists and Herpetologists.

[51] Twitty, V. C. 1935. Two new species of *Triturus* from California. *Copeia,* **1935:** 73–80.

[52] Twitty, V. C. 1942. The species of Californian *Triturus. Copeia,* **1942:** 66–76.

[53] Stebbins, R. C. 1951. *Amphibians of Western North America.* University of California Press, Berkeley. 530 p.

[54] Myers, G. S. 1942. Notes on Pacific Coast *Triturus. Copeia,* 1942: 77–82.

[55] Bishop, S. C. 1943. *Handbook of Salamanders: the Salamanders of the United States, of Canada, and of Lower California.* Comstock Publishing Co., Ithaca. 555 p.

[56] Schmidt, Karl P. 1953. *A Check List of North American Amphibians and Reptiles*, Sixth Edition. University of Chicago Press, Chicago. 280 p.

[57] Riemer, W. J. 1958. Variation and systematic relationships within the salamander genus *Taricha*. *Univ. Calif. Publ. Zool.*, **56:** 301–390.

[58] DuShane, G. P. 1935. An experimental study of the origin of pigment cells in Amphibia. *J. Exp. Zool.*, **72:** 1–31.

[59] Hörstadius, S. 1950. *The Neural Crest*. Oxford University Press, Oxford, England. 111 p.

[60] Twitty, V. C. 1936. Correlated genetic and embryological experiments on *Triturus*. I. Hybridization: development of 3 species of *Triturus* and their hybrid combinations. II. Transplantation: the embryological basis of species differences in pigment pattern. *J. Exp. Zool.*, **74:** 239–302.

[61] Twitty, V. C., and D. Bodenstein. 1939. Correlated genetic and embryological experiments on *Triturus*. III. Further transplantation experiments on pigment development. IV. The study of pigment cell behavior *in vitro*. *J. Exp. Zool.*, **81:** 357–398.

[62] Twitty, V. C. 1949. Developmental analysis of amphibian pigmentation. *Growth Symposium*, **9:** 133–161.

[63] Twitty, V. C. 1953. Intercellular relations in the development of amphibian pigmentation. *J. Embryol. Exp. Morph.* **1:** 263–268.

[64] Dalton, H. C. 1950. Inhibition of chromatoblast migration as a factor in the development of genetic differences in pigmentation in white and black axolotls. *J. Exp. Zool.*, **115:** 151–174.

[65] Lehman, H. E. 1951. An analysis of the dynamic factors responsible for the phenomenon of pigment suppression in salamander larvae. *Biol. Bull.*, **100:** 127–152.

[66] Weiss, P. 1945. Experiments on cell and axon orientation *in vitro*: the role of colloidal exudates in tissue organization. *J. Exp. Zool.*, **100:** 353–386.

[67] Twitty, V. C. 1945. The developmental analysis of specific pigment patterns. *J. Exp. Zool.*, **100:** 141–178.

[68] Twitty, V. C., and M. C. Niu. 1948. Causal analysis of chromatophore migration. *J. Exp. Zool.*, **108:** 405–437.

[69] Twitty, V. C. 1944. Chromatophore migration as a response to mutual influences of the developing pigment cells. *J. Exp. Zool.*, **95:** 259–290.

[70] Algard, F. T. 1953. Morphology and migratory behavior of embryonic pigment cells studied by phase microscopy. *J. Exp. Zool.*, **123:** 499–522.

[71] Twitty, V. C., and D. Bodenstein. 1944. The effect of temporal and regional differentials on the development of grafted chromatophores. *J. Exp. Zool.*, **95:** 213–231.

[72] Lehman, H. E. 1953. Analysis of the development of pigment patterns in salamanders with special reference to the influence of epidermis and mesoderm. *J. Exp. Zool.*, **124:** 571–620.

[73] Lehman, H. E. and L. M. Youngs. 1959. P. 1–36 *in* M. Gordon, ed., *Pigment-Cell Biology*, Academic Press, New York.

[74] Twitty, V. C. 1955. Field experiments on the biology and genetic relationships of the Californian species of *Triturus*. *J. Exp. Zool.*, **129:** 129–148.

[75] Packer, W. C. 1960. Bioclimatic influences on the breeding migration of *Taricha rivularis*. *Ecology*, **41**: 509–517.

[76] Packer, W. C. 1963. Observations on the breeding migration of *Taricha rivularis*. *Copeia*, **1963**: 378–382.

[77] Packer, W. C. 1961. Feeding behavior in adult *Taricha*. *Copeia*, **1961**: 351–352.

[78] Twitty, V. C. 1959. Migration and speciation in newts. *Science*, **139**: 1735–1743.

[79] Twitty, V. C. 1961. Experiments on homing behavior and speciation in *Taricha*. P. 415–459 *in* W. F. Blair, ed., *Vertebrate Speciation*, University of Texas Press, Austin.

[80] Twitty, V. C., D. Grant, and O. Anderson. 1964. Long distance homing in the newt *Taricha rivularis*. *Proc. Nat. Acad. Sci.*, **51**: 51–59.

[81] Ferguson, D. E. 1963. Orientation in three species of anuran amphibians. *Ergebn d. Biol.* **26**: 128–134.

[82] Ferguson, D. E., H. F. Landreth, and M. R. Turinspeed. 1965. Astronomical orientation of the southern cricket frog *Acris gryllus*. *Copeia*, **1965**: 58–66.

[83] Grant, D. L. 1965. Olfaction and homing in the newt *Taricha rivularis*. Master's Dissertation, Stanford University.

[84] Bogert, C. M. 1947. A field study of homing in the Carolina toad. *Amer. Mus. Nov.*, **1355**: 1–24.

[85] Bogert, C. M. 1960. The influence of sound on the behavior of amphibians and reptiles. P. 137–320 *in* W. E. Lanyon and W. N. Tavolga, eds., *Animal Sounds and Communication* (A.I.B.S. Publ., 7). G. E. Stechert, New York.

[86] Brattstrom, B. H. 1962. Homing in the giant toad, *Bufo marinus*. *Herpetologica*, **18**: 176–180.

[87] Jameson, D. L. 1957. Population structure and homing in the Pacific tree frog. *Copeia*, **1957**: 221–228.

[88] Martof, B. S. 1962. Some observations on the role of olfaction among salientian Amphibia. *Physiol. Zool.*, **35**: 270–272.

[89] Pimentel, R. A. 1960. Inter- and intrahabitat movements of the rough-skinned newt, *Taricha torosa granulosa* (Skilton). *Amer. Midl. Nat.*, **63**: 470–496.

[90] Heusser, H. 1960. Ueber die Beziehungen der Erdkrote (*Bufo bufo* L.) zu ihrem Laichplatz:II. *Behavior*, **16**: 94–109.

[91] Heusser, H. 1964. Zur Laichplatzorientierung der Erdkrote, *Bufo bufo* L. Mitteil. *Naturforsch. Ges. Scaffhausen*, **28**: 1–12.

[92] Hasler, A. D. 1960. Guideposts of migrating fishes. *Science*, **132**: 785–792.

[93] Callan, H. G., and H. Spurway. 1951. A study of meiosis in interracial hybrids of the newt, *Triturus cristatus*. *J. Genet.*, **50**: 236–249.

[94] Kawamura, T. 1950. Studies on hybridization in amphibians. III. Reciprocal hybrids between *Triturus pyrrhogaster* and *Triturus ensicauda*. *J. Sci. Hiroshima Univ.*, Ser. B-I, **11**: 71–79.

[95] Kawamura, T. 1952. Studies on hybridization in amphibians. IV. Hybrids bebetween *Hynobius nebulosus* (Schlegel) and *Hynobius naevius* (Schlegel). *J. Sci. Hiroshima Univ.*, Ser. B-I, **13**: 139–148.

[96] Kawamura, T. 1953. Studies on hybridization in amphibians. V. Physiological isolation among four *Hynobius* species. *J. Sci. Hiroshima Univ.*, Ser. B-I, **14**: 73–116.

[97] Lantz, L. A., and H. G. Callan. 1954. Phenotypes and spermatogenesis of interspecific hybrids between *Triturus cristatus* and *Triturus marmoratus*. *J. Genet.*, **52**: 165–185.

[98] Spurway, H. 1953. Genetics of specific and subspecific differences in European newts. *Symp. Soc. Exptl. Biol.*, **7**: 200–237.

[99] Spurway, H., and H. G. Callan. 1960. The vigor and male sterility of hybrids between the species *Triturus vulgaris* and *T. helveticus*. *J. Genet.*, **57**: 84–118.

[100] White, M. J. D. 1946. The spermatogenesis of hybrids between *Triturus cristatus* and *T. marmoratus* (*Urodela*). *J. Exp. Zool.*, **102**: 179–205.

[101] Twitty, V. C. 1961. Second-generation hybrids of the species of *Taricha*. *Proc. Nat. Acad. Sci.*, **47**: 1461–1486.

[102] Twitty, V. C. 1964. Fertility of *Taricha* species-hybrids and viability of their offspring. *Proc. Nat. Acad. Sci.*, **51**: 156–161.

[103] Stebbins, G. L. 1959. The role of hybridization in evolution. *Proc. Amer. Philos. Soc.*, **103**: 231–251.

[104] Mayr, Ernst. 1963. *Animal Species and Evolution*. Harvard University Press, Cambridge. 797 p.

[105] Davis, W. C., and V. C. Twitty. 1964. Courtship behavior and reproductive isolation in the species of *Taricha* (Amphibia, Caudata). *Copeia* **1964**: 601–610.

[106] Bonner, J. T. 1952. *Morphogenesis*. Princeton University Press, Princeton. 296 p.

[107] Willier, B. H., P. A. Weiss, and V. Hamburger. 1955. *Analysis of Development*. Saunders, Philadelphia and London. 735 p.

[108] Willier, B. H., and J. M. Oppenheimer 1964. *Foundations of Experimental Embryology*. Prentice-Hall, Englewood Cliffs, N.J. 225 p.

[109] Carty, J. 1956. *Animal Navigation: How Animals Find Their Way About*. G. Allen and Unwin, London. 151 p.

[110] Matthews, G. V. T. 1955. *Bird Navigation*. Cambridge University Press, Cambridge, England. 141 p.

[111] Schmidt-Koenig, K. 1965. Current problems in bird orientation. *Advances in the Study of Behavior*, **1**: 217–278.

[112] Griffin, D. R. 1964. *Bird Migration*. Natural History Press, Garden City, New York. 180 p.

[113] McGill, T. E. 1965. *Readings in Animal Behavior*. Holt, Rinehart and Winston, New York. 592 p.

[114] Lorenz, K. 1952. *King Solomon's Ring: New Light on Animal Ways*. Crowell, New York. 202 p.

Index